THE BOOK OF PROBLEMS:

Brian K. Saltzer
Eric Stimmel

The Book of Problems Series

Printed in the United States of America

10 9 8 7 6 5 4 3 2 1

ISBN 0-536-17570-5

2006360042

DG

Please visit our web site at *www.pearsoncustom.com*

PEARSON CUSTOM PUBLISHING
75 Arlington Street, Suite 300, Boston, MA 02116
A Pearson Education Company

About This Book

The Book of Problems series originated in the fact that students simply don't need another textbook on Algebra, Precalculus, Calculus, etc. There are already wonderful textbooks on the market in almost every area of mathematics and science. What struggling students do need, however, are more detailed worked examples than are normally found in even the best textbooks. To solve this problem, every book in the Book of Problems series contains hundreds of problems with both answers and detailed, worked solutions.

In this volume, *The Book of Problems: Calculus*, each of the major concepts in a standard Calculus course is given its own section and problems. After a list of the problems for a concept, the answers are given so that students can compare their answers to the correct ones. Following the answers are detailed worked solutions to each problem. The answers are given first because many students do not want to see a detailed worked solution immediately upon finding that their answer is not the correct one.

At the end of the book are two Final Exams that test whether or not the student has grasped all of the concepts in the book. Because students must be able to solve problems regardless of the order that they appear on their college/high school exams, the Finals are not in the same concept order as that given in the Table of Contents. As with every other problem in the Book of Problems series, detailed, worked solutions to all Final Exam questions are included in the book.

Our sincere hope is that this book will aid you in your goal of attaining both a higher course grade and a deeper understanding of Calculus.

BKS
EPS

Table of Contents

RELATIONS AND FUNCTIONS

Determine which of the following relations, equations, or graphs are functions.

1. $\{(2, 5), (3, 8), (4, -1)\}$

2. $y = x^2 + 3$

3. $\{(1, 2), (-1, 5), (5, 7), (-1, 8)\}$

4.
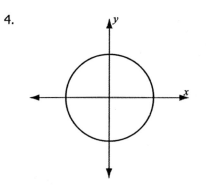

5. $y = \pm x$

6. $y = \dfrac{1}{x}$

7.
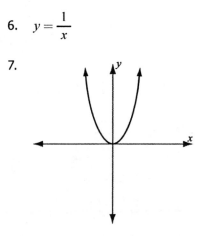

8. $\{(1, 2), (2, 2), (3, 2), (4, 2), (5, 2)\}$

9. $y^2 = x$

10.
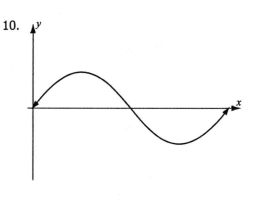

Answer Key

1. Function
2. Function
3. Not a Function
4. Not a Function
5. Not a Function
6. Function
7. Function
8. Function
9. Not a Function
10. Function

Solutions

1. $\{(2, 5), (3, 8), (4, -1)\}$

   Domain $= \{2, 3, 4\}$

   Range $= \{-1, 5, 8\}$

   The relation is also a function since each element of the domain is associated with a single element of the range.

2. $y = x^2 + 3$

   Yes, the equation is a function. Each element of the domain (the x-values) is associated with a single element of the range (the y-values that result).

3. $\{(1, 2), (-1, 5), (5, 7), (-1, 8)\}$

   Domain $= \{-1, 1, 5\}$

   Range $= \{2, 5, 7, 8\}$

   No, the relation is not a function. The domain element -1 is associated with two different range elements, 5 and 8.

4.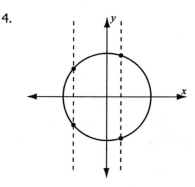

   Using the vertical line test, we see that the graph does not define a function.

5. $y = \pm x$

   No, the equation is not a function. Any x (elements of the domain) will produce two different y's (elements of the range) due to the $\pm$ sign in the equation.

6. $y = \dfrac{1}{x}$

   Yes, the equation is a function. Each element of the domain (the x-values) is associated with a single element of the range (the y-values that result).

Notes

7.

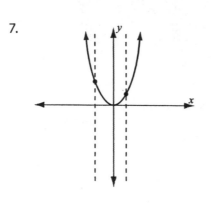

Using the vertical line test, we see that the graph is indeed a function.

8. $\{(1, 2), (2, 2), (3, 2), (4, 2), (5, 2)\}$

Domain $= \{1, 2, 3, 4, 5\}$

Range $= \{2\}$

The relation is also a function since each element of the domain is associated with a single element of the range.

9. $y^2 = x$

$\sqrt{y^2} = \sqrt{x}$

$y = \pm\sqrt{x}$

No, the equation is not a function. Any x (elements of the domain) will produce two different y's (elements of the range) due to the $\pm$ sign in the equation.

10.

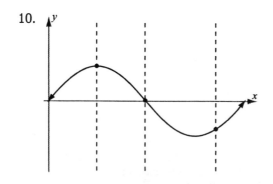

Using the vertical line test, we see that the graph is indeed a function.

Find the slope of each of the following lines.

1. $y = 6x + 1$

2. $y = -7x + \dfrac{1}{2}$

3. $y = \dfrac{1}{4}x + 12$

4. $y - 2x = 8$

5. $\dfrac{y-2}{x} = 5$

6. A line that is parallel to $y = 4x - 6$.

7. A line that is parallel to $y = -5x + 2$.

8. A line that is perpendicular to $y = 2x + 8$.

9. A line that is perpendicular to $y = -\dfrac{1}{3}x + 9$.

10. A line that passes through the point $(0, 1)$ and $(2, 5)$.

11. A line that passes through the point $(-1, -3)$ and $(-2, 4)$.

12. A line that passes through the origin and is parallel to the line $y = -6x + 10$.

13. A horizontal line.

14. A vertical line.

15. The line for which each value of the y-coordinate is 2 times the value of the x-coordinate.

Notes

1. slope $= 6$

2. slope $= -7$

3. slope $= \dfrac{1}{4}$

4. slope $= 2$

5. slope $= 5$

6. slope $= 4$

7. slope $= -5$

8. slope $= -\dfrac{1}{2}$

9. slope $= 3$

10. slope $= 2$

11. slope $= -7$

12. slope $= -6$

13. slope $= 0$

14. slope is undefined

15. slope $= 2$

Solutions

1. $y = 6x + 1$

   Since the line is already in slope-intercept form, we see that the slope is 6.

2. $y = -7x + \dfrac{1}{2}$

   slope $= -7$

3. $y = \dfrac{1}{4}x + 12$

   slope $= \dfrac{1}{4}$

4. $y - 2x = 8$

   First, we put the line into slope-intercept form:
   $$y = 2x + 8$$

   From the resulting equation we see that the slope is 2.

5. $\dfrac{y-2}{x} = 5$

   First, we put the line into slope-intercept form:
   $$\frac{y-2}{x} = 5$$
   $$y - 2 = 5x$$
   $$y = 5x + 2$$

   From the resulting equation we see that the slope is 5.

6. Since parallel lines have the same slope, a line parallel to $y = 4x - 6$ would have a slope of 4.

7. Since parallel lines have the same slope, a line parallel to $y = -5x + 2$ would have a slope of -5.

8. Since perpendicular lines have negative reciprocal slopes, a line perpendicular to $y = 2x + 8$ would have a slope of $-\dfrac{1}{2}$.

9. Since perpendicular lines have negative reciprocal slopes, a line perpendicular to $y = -\dfrac{1}{3}x + 9$ would have a slope of 3.

10. Inserting the two given points into the slope equation we get:

$$(0, 1), (2, 5)$$

$$x_1 \quad y_1 \quad x_2 \quad y_2$$

$$\text{slope} = \frac{y_2 - y_1}{x_2 - x_1}$$

$$\text{slope} = \frac{5 - 1}{2 - 0}$$

$$\text{slope} = \frac{4}{2}$$

$$\text{slope} = 2$$

11. Inserting the two given points into the slope equation we get:

$$(-1, -3), (-2, 4)$$

$$x_1 \quad y_1 \quad x_2 \quad y_2$$

$$\text{slope} = \frac{y_2 - y_1}{x_2 - x_1}$$

$$\text{slope} = \frac{4 - (-3)}{-2 - (-1)}$$

$$\text{slope} = \frac{4 + 3}{-2 + 1}$$

$$\text{slope} = \frac{7}{-1}$$

$$\text{slope} = -7$$

12. Since parallel lines must have the same slope, the fact that the line passes through the origin is extraneous. The line must have a slope of −6.

13. All horizontal lines have a slope of zero.

14. All vertical lines have an undefined slope.

15. Since each y-coordinate of a point on the line is twice the value of each corresponding x-coordinate, the line has a slope of 2.

THE LIMIT OF A FUNCTION

Calculate each of the following limits.

1. $\lim\limits_{x \to 2} (x+3)$

2. $\lim\limits_{x \to -1} x^2$

3. $\lim\limits_{x \to 0} (x^3 - x^2 + 4)$

4. $\lim\limits_{x \to \frac{1}{2}} (x + x^2)$

5. $\lim\limits_{x \to 1} \dfrac{x^2 + 3x - 1}{x^4 - x^3 + 6}$

6. $\lim\limits_{x \to 2} \dfrac{x^2 - 4}{x - 2}$

7. $\lim\limits_{x \to 3} \dfrac{x^2 - x - 6}{x - 3}$

8. $\lim\limits_{x \to 4} \dfrac{\sqrt{x} + x}{x - 5}$

9. $\lim\limits_{x \to 5} \dfrac{x^2 - 25}{x^2 - 3x - 10}$

10. $\lim\limits_{x \to -2} \dfrac{(1-x)^3 (x+2)^2}{x - 1}$

11. $\lim\limits_{x \to 2} 5$

12. $\lim\limits_{x \to -6} 4$

13. $\lim\limits_{x \to 0} \cos x$

14. $\lim\limits_{x \to \pi} \cos x$

15. $\lim\limits_{x \to \frac{\pi}{4}} \sin x$

16. $\lim\limits_{x \to \pi} \sin x$

17. $\lim\limits_{x \to \frac{\pi}{4}} \tan x$

18. $\lim\limits_{x \to \infty} \dfrac{1}{x}$

19. $\lim\limits_{x \to 0} \dfrac{1}{x}$

20. $\lim\limits_{x \to \infty} \dfrac{x^3 + 6x + 2}{4x^2 - 3x + 8}$

21. $\lim\limits_{x \to \infty} \dfrac{2x^3 - 7x^2 + 12}{3x^4 + 11x^3 + 5x^2 + 10}$

22. $\lim\limits_{x \to \infty} \dfrac{3x^2 + 5x + 2}{7x^2 - 4}$

23. $\lim\limits_{x \to 2} \dfrac{x-5}{2} + (x-3)^2 + \dfrac{x-2}{x^2 + 3x - 10}$

24. $\lim\limits_{x \to \infty} \dfrac{5}{x} + \dfrac{x^2 - x - 15}{6x^2 + 10}$

25. $\lim\limits_{x \to p} (x^2 - 2x + 3)$

Notes

Notes

Answer Key

1. $\lim_{x \to 2} (x+3) = 5$

2. $\lim_{x \to -1} x^2 = 1$

3. $\lim_{x \to 0} (x^3 - x^2 + 4) = 4$

4. $\lim_{x \to \frac{1}{2}} (x + x^2) = \frac{3}{4}$

5. $\lim_{x \to 1} \frac{x^2 + 3x - 1}{x^4 - x^3 + 6} = \frac{1}{2}$

6. $\lim_{x \to 2} \frac{x^2 - 4}{x - 2} = 4$

7. $\lim_{x \to 3} \frac{x^2 - x - 6}{x - 3} = 5$

8. $\lim_{x \to 4} \frac{\sqrt{x} + x}{x - 5} = -6$

9. $\lim_{x \to 5} \frac{x^2 - 25}{x^2 - 3x - 10} = 1\frac{3}{7}$

10. $\lim_{x \to -2} \frac{(1-x)^3 (x+2)^2}{x - 1} = 0$

11. $\lim_{x \to 2} 5 = 5$

12. $\lim_{x \to -6} 4 = 4$

13. $\lim_{x \to 0} \cos x = 1$

14. $\lim_{x \to \pi} \cos x = -1$

15. $\lim_{x \to \frac{\pi}{4}} \sin x = 0.707$

16. $\lim_{x \to \pi} \sin x = 0$

17. $\lim_{x \to \frac{\pi}{4}} \tan x = 1$

18. $\lim_{x \to \infty} \frac{1}{x} = 0$

19. $\lim_{x \to 0} \frac{1}{x} = \infty$

20. $\lim_{x \to \infty} \frac{x^3 + 6x + 2}{4x^2 - 3x + 8} = \infty$

21. $\lim_{x \to \infty} \frac{2x^3 - 7x^2 + 12}{3x^4 + 11x^3 + 5x^2 + 10} = 0$

22. $\lim_{x \to \infty} \frac{3x^2 + 5x + 2}{7x^2 - 4} = \frac{3}{7}$

23. $\lim_{x \to 2} \frac{x-5}{2} + (x-3)^2 + \frac{x-2}{x^2 + 3x - 10} = -\frac{5}{14}$

24. $\lim_{x \to \infty} \frac{5}{x} + \frac{x^2 - x - 15}{6x^2 + 10} = \frac{1}{6}$

25. $\lim_{x \to p} (x^2 - 2x + 3) = p^2 - 2p + 3$

Solutions

1. $\lim\limits_{x \to 2}(x+3) = 2+3 = 5$

2. $\lim\limits_{x \to -1} x^2 = (-1)^2 = 1$

3. $\lim\limits_{x \to 0}(x^3 - x^2 + 4) = 0^3 - 0^2 + 4 = 4$

4. $\lim\limits_{x \to \frac{1}{2}}(x + x^2) = \dfrac{1}{2} + \left(\dfrac{1}{2}\right)^2 = \dfrac{1}{2} + \dfrac{1}{4} = \dfrac{3}{4}$

5. $\lim\limits_{x \to 1}\dfrac{x^2 + 3x - 1}{x^4 - x^3 + 6} = \dfrac{1^2 + 3(1) - 1}{1^4 - 1^3 + 6} = \dfrac{3}{6} = \dfrac{1}{2}$

6. $\lim\limits_{x \to 2}\dfrac{x^2 - 4}{x - 2}$

    Although it might appear at first that we cannot directly insert $x = 2$ into the limit, if we factor the numerator we find:

    $\lim\limits_{x \to 2}\dfrac{x^2 - 4}{x - 2}$

    $\lim\limits_{x \to 2}\dfrac{(x+2)(x-2)}{x - 2}$

    $\lim\limits_{x \to 2}(x+2) = 2 + 2 = 4$

7. $\lim\limits_{x \to 3}\dfrac{x^2 - x - 6}{x - 3}$

    First factoring the numerator, we are able to find the limit at $x = 3$.

    $\lim\limits_{x \to 3}\dfrac{x^2 - x - 6}{x - 3}$

    $\lim\limits_{x \to 3}\dfrac{(x-3)(x+2)}{x - 3}$

    $\lim\limits_{x \to 3}(x+2) = 3 + 2 = 5$

8. $\lim\limits_{x \to 4}\dfrac{\sqrt{x} + x}{x - 5}$

    Keeping the principal root of the square root:

    $\lim\limits_{x \to 4}\dfrac{\sqrt{x} + x}{x - 5}$

    $\lim\limits_{x \to 4}\dfrac{\sqrt{4} + 4}{4 - 5} = \dfrac{2 + 4}{-1} = \dfrac{6}{-1} = -6$

9. $\lim\limits_{x \to 5} \dfrac{x^2 - 25}{x^2 - 3x - 10}$

Factoring both numerator and denominator we are able to find the limit at $x = 5$.

$$\lim_{x \to 5} \frac{x^2 - 25}{x^2 - 3x - 10}$$

$$\lim_{x \to 5} \frac{(x+5)(x-5)}{(x+2)(x-5)}$$

$$\lim_{x \to 5} \frac{x+5}{x+2} = \frac{5+5}{5+2} = \frac{10}{7} = 1\frac{3}{7}$$

10. $\lim\limits_{x \to -2} \dfrac{(1-x)^3 (x+2)^2}{x-1}$

$$\lim_{x \to -2} \frac{\left[1-(-2)\right]^3 (-2+2)^2}{-2-1} = \frac{(1+2)^3 (0)^2}{-3} = \frac{0}{-3} = 0$$

11. $\lim\limits_{x \to 2} 5$

Since the limit of a constant is simply the constant:

$$\lim_{x \to 2} 5 = 5$$

12. $\lim\limits_{x \to -6} 4$

Since the limit of a constant is simply the constant:

$$\lim_{x \to -6} 4 = 4$$

13. $\lim\limits_{x \to 0} \cos x = \cos 0 = 1$

14. $\lim\limits_{x \to \pi} \cos x = \cos \pi = -1$

15. $\lim\limits_{x \to \frac{\pi}{4}} \sin x = \sin \dfrac{\pi}{4} = \dfrac{\sqrt{2}}{2} \approx 0.707$

16. $\lim\limits_{x \to \pi} \sin x = \sin \pi = 0$

17. $\lim\limits_{x \to \frac{\pi}{4}} \tan x = \tan \dfrac{\pi}{4} = 1$

18. $\lim\limits_{x \to \infty} \dfrac{1}{x}$

Although we cannot directly insert infinity into the expression, we can insert larger and larger values in order to find the limiting behavior of the expression.

x	$\dfrac{1}{x}$
1	$\dfrac{1}{1} = 1$
10	$\dfrac{1}{10} = 0.1$
100	$\dfrac{1}{100} = 0.01$
1000	$\dfrac{1}{1000} = 0.001$
10,000	$\dfrac{1}{10,000} = 0.0001$
100,000	$\dfrac{1}{100,000} = 0.00001$
$\vdots$	$\vdots$

From the table we can see that as x gets larger and larger, $\dfrac{1}{x}$ gets smaller and smaller.

Thus,

$$\lim\limits_{x \to \infty} \frac{1}{x} = 0$$

19. $\lim\limits_{x \to 0} \dfrac{1}{x}$

Although we cannot insert zero since the expression is not defined at this point, we can insert smaller and smaller values in order to find the limiting behavior of the expression.

x	$\dfrac{1}{x}$
100	$\dfrac{1}{100} = 0.01$
10	$\dfrac{1}{10} = 0.1$
1	$\dfrac{1}{1} = 1$
0.1	$\dfrac{1}{0.1} = 10$
0.01	$\dfrac{1}{0.01} = 100$
0.001	$\dfrac{1}{0.001} = 1000$
$\vdots$	$\vdots$

From the table we can see that as x gets smaller and smaller, $\dfrac{1}{x}$ gets larger and larger.

Thus,

$$\lim_{x \to 0} \frac{1}{x} = \infty$$

20. $\lim\limits_{x \to \infty} \dfrac{x^3 + 6x + 2}{4x^2 - 3x + 8}$

The limiting behavior of this expression becomes apparent if we divide all terms by the term *one lower* than the highest exponent, in the expression.

$\Rightarrow \quad \lim\limits_{x \to \infty} \dfrac{x^3 + 6x + 2}{4x^2 - 3x + 8}$

$\lim\limits_{x \to \infty} \dfrac{x^3 + 6x + 2}{4x^2 - 3x + 8} \cdot \dfrac{\frac{1}{x^2}}{\frac{1}{x^2}}$

$\lim\limits_{x \to \infty} \dfrac{\dfrac{x^3}{x^2} + \dfrac{6x}{x^2} + \dfrac{2}{x^2}}{\dfrac{4x^2}{x^2} - \dfrac{3x}{x^2} + \dfrac{8}{x^2}}$

$\lim\limits_{x \to \infty} \dfrac{x + \dfrac{6}{x} + \dfrac{2}{x^2}}{4 - \dfrac{3}{x} + \dfrac{8}{x^2}}$

calculation cont. on next page...

Solution #20 from previous page...

From Problem #18 we know that $\lim\limits_{x \to \infty} \dfrac{1}{x} = 0$.

Thus,

$$\lim_{x \to \infty} \frac{x + \overset{0}{\cancel{\dfrac{6}{x}}} + \overset{0}{\cancel{\dfrac{2}{x^2}}}}{4 - \underset{0}{\cancel{\dfrac{3}{x}}} + \underset{0}{\cancel{\dfrac{8}{x^2}}}}$$

The effective portion of the limit therefore reduces to:

$$\lim_{x \to \infty} \frac{x}{4} = \infty$$

Thus,

$$\lim_{x \to \infty} \frac{x^3 + 6x + 2}{4x^2 - 3x + 8} = \infty$$

21. $\lim\limits_{x \to \infty} \dfrac{2x^3 - 7x^2 + 12}{3x^4 + 11x^3 + 5x^2 + 10}$

As we did in Problem #20, we divide all terms by x raised to one lower power than the highest exponent in the limit, namely x^3.

$$\lim_{x \to \infty} \frac{2x^3 - 7x^2 + 12}{3x^4 + 11x^3 + 5x^2 + 10} \cdot \frac{\dfrac{1}{x^3}}{\dfrac{1}{x^3}}$$

$$\lim_{x \to \infty} \frac{\dfrac{2x^3}{x^3} - \dfrac{7x^2}{x^3} + \dfrac{12}{x^3}}{\dfrac{3x^4}{x^3} + \dfrac{11x^3}{x^3} + \dfrac{5x^2}{x^3} + \dfrac{10}{x^3}}$$

$$\lim_{x \to \infty} \frac{2 - \dfrac{7}{x} + \dfrac{12}{x^3}}{3x + 11 + \dfrac{5}{x} + \dfrac{10}{x^3}}$$

From Problem #18 we know that $\lim\limits_{x \to \infty} \dfrac{1}{x} = 0$.

Thus,

$$\lim_{x \to \infty} \frac{2 - \overset{0}{\cancel{\dfrac{7}{x}}} + \overset{0}{\cancel{\dfrac{12}{x^3}}}}{3x + 11 + \underset{0}{\cancel{\dfrac{5}{x}}} + \underset{0}{\cancel{\dfrac{10}{x^3}}}}$$

calculation cont. on next page...

Solution #21 from previous page...

The effective portion of the limit is therefore:

$$\lim_{x \to \infty} \frac{2}{3x+11} = 0$$

Thus,

$$\lim_{x \to \infty} \frac{2x^3 - 7x^2 + 12}{3x^4 + 11x^3 + 5x^2 + 10} = 0$$

22. $\lim\limits_{x \to \infty} \dfrac{3x^2 + 5x + 2}{7x^2 - 4}$

Since the orders of both the numerator and the denominator are the same, we divide all terms by x^2.

$$\lim_{x \to \infty} \frac{3x^2 + 5x + 2}{7x^2 - 4} \cdot \frac{\dfrac{1}{x^2}}{\dfrac{1}{x^2}}$$

$$\lim_{x \to \infty} \frac{\dfrac{3x^2}{x^2} + \dfrac{5x}{x^2} + \dfrac{2}{x^2}}{\dfrac{7x^2}{x^2} - \dfrac{4}{x^2}}$$

$$\lim_{x \to \infty} \frac{3 + \dfrac{5}{x} + \dfrac{2}{x^2}}{7 - \dfrac{4}{x^2}}$$

From Problem #18 we know that $\lim\limits_{x \to \infty} \dfrac{1}{x} = 0$.

Thus,

$$\lim_{x \to \infty} \frac{3 + \overset{0}{\cancel{\dfrac{5}{x}}} + \overset{0}{\cancel{\dfrac{2}{x^2}}}}{7 - \underset{0}{\cancel{\dfrac{4}{x^2}}}}$$

Reducing the effective portion of the limit to:

$$\lim_{x \to \infty} \frac{3}{7}$$

From Problems #11 and #12 we know that the limit of a constant is simply the constant.

$$\Rightarrow \lim_{x \to \infty} \frac{3}{7} = \frac{3}{7}$$

Thus,

$$\lim_{x \to \infty} \frac{3x^2 + 5x + 2}{7x^2 - 4} = \frac{3}{7}$$

Notice that when the orders of the numerator and denominator are equal, the limit becomes the ratio of the lead coefficients.

23. $\lim\limits_{x \to 2} \dfrac{x-5}{2} + (x-3)^2 + \dfrac{x-2}{x^2+3x-10}$

We begin by factoring the denominator of the 3rd term simplifying the limit to:

$$\lim\limits_{x \to 2} \dfrac{x-5}{2} + (x-3)^2 + \dfrac{\cancel{x-2}}{\cancel{(x-2)}(x+5)}$$

$$\lim\limits_{x \to 2} \dfrac{x-5}{2} + (x-3)^2 + \dfrac{1}{x+5}$$

Substituting $x = 2$ we find the limit of the entire expression.

$$\lim\limits_{x \to 2} \dfrac{x-5}{2} + (x-3)^2 + \dfrac{1}{x+5}$$

$$\lim\limits_{x \to 2} \dfrac{2-5}{2} + (2-3)^2 + \dfrac{1}{2+5}$$

$$\lim\limits_{x \to 2} \dfrac{-3}{2} + (-1)^2 + \dfrac{1}{7}$$

$$\lim\limits_{x \to 2} -\dfrac{3}{2} + 1 + \dfrac{1}{7}$$

$$\lim\limits_{x \to 2} -\dfrac{1}{2} + \dfrac{1}{7} = -\dfrac{5}{14}$$

24. $\lim\limits_{x \to \infty} \dfrac{5}{x} + \dfrac{x^2-x-15}{6x^2+10}$

This problem is simply a combination of Problems #18 and #22. From Problem #18 we know that the limit of the first term is zero:

$$\lim\limits_{x \to \infty} \dfrac{\overset{0}{\cancel{5}}}{\cancel{x}} + \dfrac{x^2-x-15}{6x^2+10}$$

reducing the effective expression to:

$$\lim\limits_{x \to \infty} \dfrac{x^2-x-15}{6x^2+10}$$

From Problem #22 we know that when the orders of the numerator and the denominator are the same, the limit becomes the ratio of the lead coefficients.

Thus,

$$\lim\limits_{x \to \infty} \dfrac{x^2-x-15}{6x^2+10} = \dfrac{(1)x^2-x-15}{6x^2+10} = \dfrac{1}{6}$$

The total limit therefore becomes:

$$\lim\limits_{x \to \infty} \dfrac{5}{x} + \dfrac{x^2-x-15}{6x^2+10} = \dfrac{1}{6}$$

25. $\lim\limits_{x \to p} (x^2 - 2x + 3) = p^2 - 2p + 3$

THE DEFINITION OF THE DERIVATIVE

Using the definition of the derivative, $f'(x) = \lim\limits_{\Delta x \to 0} \dfrac{f(x + \Delta x) - f(x)}{\Delta x}$, calculate the derivative of each of the following.

1. $f(x) = x^2$

2. $f(x) = 5x$

3. $f(x) = 4x^2$

4. $f(x) = x^3$

5. $f(x) = 3x^2 + 4x$

6. $f(x) = 12$

7. $f(x) = 8$

8. $f(x) = x^4 + 8$

9. $f(x) = \sqrt{x}$

10. $f(x) = \dfrac{1}{x^3}$

Notes

Answer Key

1. $f'(x) = 2x$

2. $f'(x) = 5$

3. $f'(x) = 8x$

4. $f'(x) = 3x^2$

5. $f'(x) = 6x + 4$

6. $f'(x) = 0$

7. $f'(x) = 0$

8. $f'(x) = 4x^3$

9. $f'(x) = \dfrac{1}{2\sqrt{x}}$ or $f'(x) = \dfrac{\sqrt{x}}{2x}$

10. $f'(x) = \dfrac{-3}{x^4}$

Solutions

1. $f(x) = x^2$

$$f'(x) = \lim_{\Delta x \to 0} \frac{f(x + \Delta x) - f(x)}{\Delta x}$$

$$f'(x) = \lim_{\Delta x \to 0} \frac{(x + \Delta x)^2 - x^2}{\Delta x}$$

$$f'(x) = \lim_{\Delta x \to 0} \frac{x^2 + 2x\Delta x + (\Delta x)^2 - x^2}{\Delta x}$$

$$f'(x) = \lim_{\Delta x \to 0} \frac{2x\Delta x + (\Delta x)^2}{\Delta x}$$

$$f'(x) = \lim_{\Delta x \to 0} \frac{\Delta x (2x + \Delta x)}{\Delta x}$$

$$f'(x) = \lim_{\Delta x \to 0} (2x + \Delta x)$$

$$f'(x) = 2x$$

2. $f(x) = 5x$

$$f'(x) = \lim_{\Delta x \to 0} \frac{f(x + \Delta x) - f(x)}{\Delta x}$$

$$f'(x) = \lim_{\Delta x \to 0} \frac{5(x + \Delta x) - 5x}{\Delta x}$$

$$f'(x) = \lim_{\Delta x \to 0} \frac{5x + 5\Delta x - 5x}{\Delta x}$$

$$f'(x) = \lim_{\Delta x \to 0} \frac{5\Delta x}{\Delta x}$$

$$f'(x) = \lim_{\Delta x \to 0} 5$$

$$f'(x) = 5$$

3. $f(x) = 4x^2$

$$f'(x) = \lim_{\Delta x \to 0} \frac{f(x + \Delta x) - f(x)}{\Delta x}$$

$$f'(x) = \lim_{\Delta x \to 0} \frac{4(x + \Delta x)^2 - 4x^2}{\Delta x}$$

$$f'(x) = \lim_{\Delta x \to 0} \frac{4\left[x^2 + 2x\Delta x + (\Delta x)^2\right] - 4x^2}{\Delta x}$$

$$f'(x) = \lim_{\Delta x \to 0} \frac{4x^2 + 8x\Delta x + 4(\Delta x)^2 - 4x^2}{\Delta x}$$

$$f'(x) = \lim_{\Delta x \to 0} \frac{8x\Delta x + 4(\Delta x)^2}{\Delta x}$$

$$f'(x) = \lim_{\Delta x \to 0} \frac{\Delta x(8x + 4\Delta x)}{\Delta x}$$

$$f'(x) = \lim_{\Delta x \to 0} (8x + 4\Delta x)$$

$$f'(x) = 8x$$

4. $f(x) = x^3$

$$f'(x) = \lim_{\Delta x \to 0} \frac{f(x + \Delta x) - f(x)}{\Delta x}$$

$$f'(x) = \lim_{\Delta x \to 0} \frac{(x + \Delta x)^3 - x^3}{\Delta x}$$

$$f'(x) = \lim_{\Delta x \to 0} \frac{x^3 + 3x^2\Delta x + 3x(\Delta x)^2 + (\Delta x)^3 - x^3}{\Delta x}$$

$$f'(x) = \lim_{\Delta x \to 0} \frac{3x^2\Delta x + 3x(\Delta x)^2 + (\Delta x)^3}{\Delta x}$$

$$f'(x) = \lim_{\Delta x \to 0} \frac{\Delta x\left[3x^2 + 3x\Delta x + (\Delta x)^2\right]}{\Delta x}$$

$$f'(x) = \lim_{\Delta x \to 0} \left[3x^2 + 3x\Delta x + (\Delta x)^2\right]$$

$$f'(x) = 3x^2$$

5. $f(x) = 3x^2 + 4x$

$$f'(x) = \lim_{\Delta x \to 0} \frac{f(x + \Delta x) - f(x)}{\Delta x}$$

$$f'(x) = \lim_{\Delta x \to 0} \frac{3(x + \Delta x)^2 + 4(x + \Delta x) - (3x^2 + 4x)}{\Delta x}$$

$$f'(x) = \lim_{\Delta x \to 0} \frac{3\left[x^2 + 2x\Delta x + (\Delta x)^2\right] + 4x + 4\Delta x - 3x^2 - 4x}{\Delta x}$$

$$f'(x) = \lim_{\Delta x \to 0} \frac{3x^2 + 6x\Delta x + 3(\Delta x)^2 + 4\Delta x - 3x^2}{\Delta x}$$

$$f'(x) = \lim_{\Delta x \to 0} \frac{6x\Delta x + 3(\Delta x)^2 + 4\Delta x}{\Delta x}$$

$$f'(x) = \lim_{\Delta x \to 0} \frac{\Delta x(6x + 3\Delta x + 4)}{\Delta x}$$

$$f'(x) = \lim_{\Delta x \to 0} (6x + 3\Delta x + 4)$$

$$f'(x) = 6x + 4$$

6. $f(x) = 12$

$$f'(x) = \lim_{\Delta x \to 0} \frac{f(x + \Delta x) - f(x)}{\Delta x}$$

$$f'(x) = \lim_{\Delta x \to 0} \frac{12 - 12}{\Delta x}$$

$$f'(x) = \lim_{\Delta x \to 0} \frac{0}{\Delta x}$$

$$f'(x) = \lim_{\Delta x \to 0} 0$$

$$f'(x) = 0$$

7. $f(x) = 8$

$$f'(x) = \lim_{\Delta x \to 0} \frac{f(x + \Delta x) - f(x)}{\Delta x}$$

$$f'(x) = \lim_{\Delta x \to 0} \frac{8 - 8}{\Delta x}$$

$$f'(x) = \lim_{\Delta x \to 0} \frac{0}{\Delta x}$$

$$f'(x) = \lim_{\Delta x \to 0} 0$$

$$f'(x) = 0$$

8. $f(x) = x^4 + 8$

$$f'(x) = \lim_{\Delta x \to 0} \frac{f(x + \Delta x) - f(x)}{\Delta x}$$

$$f'(x) = \lim_{\Delta x \to 0} \frac{(x + \Delta x)^4 - x^4}{\Delta x}$$

$$f'(x) = \lim_{\Delta x \to 0} \frac{x^4 + 4x^3 \Delta x + 6x^2 (\Delta x)^2 + 4x (\Delta x)^3 + (\Delta x)^4 - x^4}{\Delta x}$$

$$f'(x) = \lim_{\Delta x \to 0} \frac{4x^3 \Delta x + 6x^2 (\Delta x)^2 + 4x (\Delta x)^3 + (\Delta x)^4}{\Delta x}$$

$$f'(x) = \lim_{\Delta x \to 0} \frac{\Delta x \left[4x^3 + 6x^2 \Delta x + 4x (\Delta x)^2 + (\Delta x)^3 \right]}{\Delta x}$$

$$f'(x) = \lim_{\Delta x \to 0} \left[4x^3 + 6x^2 \Delta x + 4x (\Delta x)^2 + (\Delta x)^3 \right]$$

$$f'(x) = 4x^3$$

9. $f(x) = \sqrt{x}$

$$f'(x) = \lim_{\Delta x \to 0} \frac{f(x + \Delta x) - f(x)}{\Delta x}$$

$$f'(x) = \lim_{\Delta x \to 0} \frac{\sqrt{x + \Delta x} - \sqrt{x}}{\Delta x}$$

$$f'(x) = \lim_{\Delta x \to 0} \frac{\sqrt{x + \Delta x} - \sqrt{x}}{\Delta x} \cdot \frac{\sqrt{x + \Delta x} + \sqrt{x}}{\sqrt{x + \Delta x} + \sqrt{x}}$$

$$f'(x) = \lim_{\Delta x \to 0} \frac{\sqrt{x + \Delta x} \cdot \sqrt{x + \Delta x} + \sqrt{x + \Delta x} \cdot \sqrt{x} - \sqrt{x} \cdot \sqrt{x + \Delta x} - \sqrt{x} \cdot \sqrt{x}}{\Delta x \left(\sqrt{x + \Delta x} + \sqrt{x} \right)}$$

$$f'(x) = \lim_{\Delta x \to 0} \frac{(x + \Delta x) + \sqrt{x^2 + x\Delta x} - \sqrt{x^2 + x\Delta x} - x}{\Delta x \left(\sqrt{x + \Delta x} + \sqrt{x} \right)}$$

$$f'(x) = \lim_{\Delta x \to 0} \frac{x + \Delta x - x}{\Delta x \left(\sqrt{x + \Delta x} + \sqrt{x} \right)}$$

$$f'(x) = \lim_{\Delta x \to 0} \frac{\Delta x}{\Delta x \left(\sqrt{x + \Delta x} + \sqrt{x} \right)}$$

$$f'(x) = \lim_{\Delta x \to 0} \frac{1}{\sqrt{x + \Delta x} + \sqrt{x}}$$

$$f'(x) = \lim_{\Delta x \to 0} \frac{1}{\sqrt{x} + \sqrt{x}}$$

$$f'(x) = \frac{1}{2\sqrt{x}}$$

Or, rationalizing the denominator:

$$f'(x) = \frac{1}{2\sqrt{x}} \cdot \frac{\sqrt{x}}{\sqrt{x}}$$

$$f'(x) = \frac{\sqrt{x}}{2x}$$

Notes

10. $f(x) = \dfrac{1}{x^3}$

$$f'(x) = \lim_{\Delta x \to 0} \frac{f(x + \Delta x) - f(x)}{\Delta x}$$

$$f'(x) = \lim_{\Delta x \to 0} \frac{\dfrac{1}{(x + \Delta x)^3} - \dfrac{1}{x^3}}{\Delta x}$$

$$f'(x) = \lim_{\Delta x \to 0} \frac{\dfrac{x^3 - (x + \Delta x)^3}{x^3 (x + \Delta x)^3}}{\Delta x}$$

$$f'(x) = \lim_{\Delta x \to 0} \frac{\dfrac{x^3 - \left[x^3 + 3x^2 \Delta x + 3x (\Delta x)^2 + (\Delta x)^3 \right]}{x^3 (x + \Delta x)^3}}{\Delta x}$$

$$f'(x) = \lim_{\Delta x \to 0} \frac{\dfrac{x^3 - x^3 - 3x^2 \Delta x - 3x (\Delta x)^2 - (\Delta x)^3}{x^3 (x + \Delta x)^3}}{\Delta x}$$

$$f'(x) = \lim_{\Delta x \to 0} \frac{\dfrac{-3x^2 \Delta x - 3x (\Delta x)^2 - (\Delta x)^3}{x^3 (x + \Delta x)^3}}{\Delta x}$$

$$f'(x) = \lim_{\Delta x \to 0} \frac{\dfrac{\Delta x \left[-3x^2 - 3x \Delta x - (\Delta x)^2 \right]}{x^3 (x + \Delta x)^3}}{\Delta x}$$

$$f'(x) = \lim_{\Delta x \to 0} \frac{\Delta x \left[-3x^2 - 3x \Delta x - (\Delta x)^2 \right]}{x^3 (x + \Delta x)^3} \cdot \frac{1}{\Delta x}$$

$$f'(x) = \lim_{\Delta x \to 0} \frac{-3x^2 - 3x \Delta x - (\Delta x)^2}{x^3 (x + \Delta x)^3}$$

$$f'(x) = \frac{-3x^2}{x^3 (x^3)}$$

$$f'(x) = \frac{-3x^2}{x^6}$$

$$f'(x) = \frac{-3}{x^4}$$

DERIVATIVES OF POLYNOMIALS

Find the derivative of each of the following polynomials.

1. $f(x) = 3x$

2. $f(x) = 2x + 5$

3. $f(x) = x^2$

4. $f(x) = x^3$

5. $f(x) = 4x^2$

6. $f(x) = 3x^2 - 6x + 2$

7. $f(x) = \dfrac{2}{3}x^6 - \dfrac{1}{2}x^4$

8. $f(x) = \sqrt{x}$

9. $f(x) = \sqrt[3]{x}$

10. $f(x) = \dfrac{5}{x^2}$

11. $f(x) = \dfrac{1}{x^3}$

12. $f(x) = \dfrac{7}{\sqrt{x}}$

13. $f(x) = \dfrac{3}{5\sqrt[3]{x}}$

14. $f(x) = x^5 - x^4 + \dfrac{2}{\sqrt{x}} - \dfrac{3}{x^8}$

15. $f(x) = 2.6x^2 + 3.1x - 5.28$

Answer Key

1. $f'(x) = 3$

2. $f'(x) = 2$

3. $f'(x) = 2x$

4. $f'(x) = 3x^2$

5. $f'(x) = 8x$

6. $f'(x) = 6x - 6$

7. $f'(x) = 4x^5 - 2x^3$

8. $f'(x) = \dfrac{1}{2\sqrt{x}}$ or $f'(x) = \dfrac{\sqrt{x}}{2x}$

9. $f'(x) = \dfrac{1}{3\sqrt[3]{x^2}}$ or $f'(x) = \dfrac{\sqrt[3]{x}}{3x}$

10. $f'(x) = \dfrac{-10}{x^3}$

11. $f'(x) = \dfrac{-3}{x^4}$

12. $f'(x) = -\dfrac{7}{2x\sqrt{x}}$ or $f'(x) = -\dfrac{7\sqrt{x}}{2x^2}$

13. $f'(x) = -\dfrac{1}{5x\sqrt[3]{x}}$ or $f'(x) = -\dfrac{\sqrt[3]{x^2}}{5x^2}$

14. $f'(x) = 5x^4 - 4x^3 - \dfrac{1}{x\sqrt{x}} + \dfrac{24}{x^9}$ or $f'(x) = 5x^4 - 4x^3 - \dfrac{\sqrt{x}}{x^2} + \dfrac{24}{x^9}$

15. $f'(x) = 5.2x + 3.1$

Solutions

1. $f(x) = 3x^1$

    $f'(x) = 1(3)x^{1-1}$

    $f'(x) = 3x^0$

    $f'(x) = 3(1)$

    $f'(x) = 3$

2. $f(x) = 2x^1 + 5$

    $f'(x) = 1(2)x^{1-1} + 0$

    $f'(x) = 2x^0$

    $f'(x) = 2(1)$

    $f'(x) = 2$

3. $f(x) = x^2$

    $f'(x) = 2x^{2-1}$

    $f'(x) = 2x^1$

    $f'(x) = 2x$

4. $f(x) = x^3$

    $f'(x) = 3x^{3-1}$

    $f'(x) = 3x^2$

5. $f(x) = 4x^2$

    $f'(x) = 2(4)x^{2-1}$

    $f'(x) = 8x^1$

    $f'(x) = 8x$

6. $f(x) = 3x^2 - 6x^1 + 2$

    $f'(x) = 2(3)x^{2-1} - 1(6)x^{1-1} + 0$

    $f'(x) = 6x^1 - 6x^0$

    $f'(x) = 6x - 6(1)$

    $f'(x) = 6x - 6$

7. $f(x) = \dfrac{2}{3}x^6 - \dfrac{1}{2}x^4$

    $f'(x) = 6\left(\dfrac{2}{3}\right)x^{6-1} - 4\left(\dfrac{1}{2}\right)x^{4-1}$

    $f'(x) = \dfrac{12}{3}x^5 - \dfrac{4}{2}x^3$

    $f'(x) = 4x^5 - 2x^3$

8. $f(x) = \sqrt{x} = \sqrt{x^1} = x^{\frac{1}{2}}$

    $f'(x) = \dfrac{1}{2}x^{\frac{1}{2}-1}$

    $f'(x) = \dfrac{1}{2}x^{-\frac{1}{2}}$

    $f'(x) = \dfrac{1}{2x^{\frac{1}{2}}}$

    $f'(x) = \dfrac{1}{2\sqrt{x}}$

    Or, rationalizing the denominator:

    $f'(x) = \dfrac{1}{2\sqrt{x}} \cdot \dfrac{\sqrt{x}}{\sqrt{x}}$

    $f'(x) = \dfrac{\sqrt{x}}{2x}$

9. $f(x) = \sqrt[3]{x} = \sqrt[3]{x^1} = x^{\frac{1}{3}}$

$f'(x) = \frac{1}{3} x^{\frac{1}{3}-1}$

$f'(x) = \frac{1}{3} x^{-\frac{2}{3}}$

$f'(x) = \frac{1}{3x^{\frac{2}{3}}}$

$f'(x) = \frac{1}{3\sqrt[3]{x^2}}$

Or, rationalizing the denominator:

$f'(x) = \frac{1}{3\sqrt[3]{x^2}} \cdot \frac{\sqrt[3]{x}}{\sqrt[3]{x}}$

$f'(x) = \frac{\sqrt[3]{x}}{3\sqrt[3]{x^2}\sqrt[3]{x}}$

$f'(x) = \frac{\sqrt[3]{x}}{3\sqrt[3]{x^3}}$

$f'(x) = \frac{\sqrt[3]{x}}{3x}$

10. $f(x) = \frac{5}{x^2} = 5x^{-2}$

$f'(x) = -2(5)x^{-2-1}$

$f'(x) = -10x^{-3}$

$f'(x) = \frac{-10}{x^3}$

11. $f(x) = \frac{1}{x^3} = x^{-3}$

$f'(x) = -3x^{-3-1}$

$f'(x) = -3x^{-4}$

$f'(x) = \frac{-3}{x^4}$

12. $f(x) = \frac{7}{\sqrt{x}} = \frac{7}{x^{\frac{1}{2}}} = 7x^{-\frac{1}{2}}$

$f'(x) = -\frac{1}{2}(7)x^{-\frac{1}{2}-1}$

$f'(x) = -\frac{7}{2}x^{-\frac{3}{2}}$

$f'(x) = -\frac{7}{2x^{\frac{3}{2}}}$

$f'(x) = -\frac{7}{2x\sqrt{x}}$

Or, rationalizing the denominator:

$f'(x) = -\frac{7}{2x\sqrt{x}} \cdot \frac{\sqrt{x}}{\sqrt{x}}$

$f'(x) = -\frac{7\sqrt{x}}{2x^2}$

13. $f(x) = \frac{3}{5\sqrt[3]{x}} = \frac{3}{5x^{\frac{1}{3}}} = \frac{3}{5}x^{-\frac{1}{3}}$

$f'(x) = -\frac{1}{3}\left(\frac{3}{5}\right)x^{-\frac{1}{3}-1}$

$f'(x) = -\frac{1}{5}x^{-\frac{4}{3}}$

$f'(x) = -\frac{1}{5x^{\frac{4}{3}}}$

$f'(x) = -\frac{1}{5x\sqrt[3]{x}}$

Or, rationalizing the denominator:

$f'(x) = -\frac{1}{5x\sqrt[3]{x}} \cdot \frac{\sqrt[3]{x^2}}{\sqrt[3]{x^2}}$

$f'(x) = -\frac{\sqrt[3]{x^2}}{5x^2}$

14. $f(x) = x^5 - x^4 + \dfrac{2}{\sqrt{x}} - \dfrac{3}{x^8}$

$f(x) = x^5 - x^4 + \dfrac{2}{x^{\frac{1}{2}}} - 3x^{-8}$

$f(x) = x^5 - x^4 + 2x^{-\frac{1}{2}} - 3x^{-8}$

$f'(x) = 5x^{5-1} - 4x^{4-1} + \left(-\dfrac{1}{2}\right)(2)x^{-\frac{1}{2}-1} + (-8)(-3)x^{-8-1}$

$f'(x) = 5x^4 - 4x^3 - x^{-\frac{3}{2}} + 24x^{-9}$

$f'(x) = 5x^4 - 4x^3 - \dfrac{1}{x^{\frac{3}{2}}} + \dfrac{24}{x^9}$

$f'(x) = 5x^4 - 4x^3 - \dfrac{1}{x\sqrt{x}} + \dfrac{24}{x^9}$

Or, rationalizing the denominator:

$f'(x) = 5x^4 - 4x^3 - \dfrac{1}{x\sqrt{x}} \cdot \dfrac{\sqrt{x}}{\sqrt{x}} + \dfrac{24}{x^9}$

$f'(x) = 5x^4 - 4x^3 - \dfrac{\sqrt{x}}{x^2} + \dfrac{24}{x^9}$

15. $f(x) = 2.6x^2 + 3.1x^1 - 5.28$

$f'(x) = 2(2.6)x^{2-1} + 1(3.1)x^{1-1} + 0$

$f'(x) = 5.2x^1 + 3.1x^0$

$f'(x) = 5.2x + 3.1(1)$

$f'(x) = 5.2x + 3.1$

PRODUCT RULE, QUOTIENT RULE, AND POWER RULE I: SIMPLE POLYNOMIALS

Use the Product Rule to find the derivative of each of the following functions.

1. $f(x) = (x^2 + 3x)(x^3 - 7x + 3)$

2. $f(x) = (2x^3 - 3x + 8)(x^4 + 6x^3 + 9x)$

3. $f(x) = \left(\frac{1}{4}x^2 - \frac{1}{3}x\right)\left(\frac{2}{5}x^4 + \frac{1}{2}x^2 - \frac{3}{8}\right)$

4. $f(x) = \left(\sqrt{x} + \frac{1}{x^3}\right)(3x + 8)$

5. $f(x) = (3.2x^5 - 4.1x^3 + 0.5x)(6.3x^3 + 2.8x^2)$

Use the Quotient Rule to find the derivative of each of the following functions.

6. $f(x) = \dfrac{x^2 + 2}{3x - 5}$

7. $f(x) = \dfrac{x^2 + 5x + 6}{x^4 - x^3}$

8. $f(x) = \dfrac{\frac{1}{2}x + 8}{x^3 - x}$

9. $f(x) = \dfrac{3}{x^5 + 6x^4 + 2x}$

10 $f(x) = \dfrac{\sqrt{x} + \frac{6}{x^3}}{4\sqrt[3]{x}}$

Use the Power Rule to find the derivative of each of the following functions.

11. $f(x) = (x^2 + 4x + 6)^3$

12. $f(x) = (5x^3 - x)^5$

13. $f(x) = \sqrt{8x^2 - 11x + 1}$

14. $f(x) = \dfrac{1}{(x^3 + 10x^2)^4}$

15 $f(x) = 7(x^6 - x^4 + x^2)^8$

Solutions

* **Note that the solutions in this section have specifically *not* been simplified so that you can see the individual pieces of each rule.**

The Product Rule

1. Multiply the 1st term in the product by the derivative of the second term in the product.
2. Add the 2nd term in the product multiplied by the derivative of the first term in the product.

1. $f(x) = \underbrace{(x^2+3x)}_{1^{st}\ term}\underbrace{(x^3-7x+3)}_{2^{nd}\ term}$

$f'(x) = \underbrace{(x^2+3x)}_{1^{st}\ term}\underbrace{(3x^2-7)}_{\substack{derivative\ of\ the\\2^{nd}\ term}} + \underbrace{(x^3-7x+3)}_{2^{nd}\ term}\underbrace{(2x+3)}_{\substack{derivative\ of\ the\\1^{st}\ term}}$

2. $f(x) = \underbrace{(2x^3-3x+8)}_{1^{st}\ term}\underbrace{(x^4+6x^3+9x)}_{2^{nd}\ term}$

$f'(x) = \underbrace{(2x^3-3x+8)}_{1^{st}\ term}\underbrace{(4x^3+18x^2+9)}_{\substack{derivative\ of\ the\\2^{nd}\ term}} + \underbrace{(x^4+6x^3+9x)}_{2^{nd}\ term}\underbrace{(6x^2-3)}_{\substack{derivative\ of\ the\\1^{st}\ term}}$

3. $f(x) = \underbrace{\left(\dfrac{1}{4}x^2-\dfrac{1}{3}x\right)}_{1^{st}\ term}\underbrace{\left(\dfrac{2}{5}x^4+\dfrac{1}{2}x^2-\dfrac{3}{8}\right)}_{2^{nd}\ term}$

$f'(x) = \underbrace{\left(\dfrac{1}{4}x^2-\dfrac{1}{3}x\right)}_{1^{st}\ term}\underbrace{\left(\dfrac{8}{5}x^3+x\right)}_{\substack{derivative\ of\ the\\2^{nd}\ term}} + \underbrace{\left(\dfrac{2}{5}x^4+\dfrac{1}{2}x^2-\dfrac{3}{8}\right)}_{2^{nd}\ term}\underbrace{\left(\dfrac{1}{2}x-\dfrac{1}{3}\right)}_{\substack{derivative\ of\ the\\1^{st}\ term}}$

4. $f(x) = \left(\sqrt{x}+\dfrac{1}{x^3}\right)(3x+8)$

$f(x) = \underbrace{\left(x^{\frac{1}{2}}+x^{-3}\right)}_{1^{st}\ term}\underbrace{(3x+8)}_{2^{nd}\ term}$

$f'(x) = \underbrace{\left(x^{\frac{1}{2}}+x^{-3}\right)}_{1^{st}\ term}\underbrace{(3)}_{\substack{derivative\ of\ the\\2^{nd}\ term}} + \underbrace{(3x+8)}_{2^{nd}\ term}\underbrace{\left(\dfrac{1}{2}x^{-\frac{1}{2}}-3x^{-4}\right)}_{\substack{derivative\ of\ the\\1^{st}\ term}}$

5. $f(x) = \underbrace{\left(3.2x^5 - 4.1x^3 + 0.5x\right)}_{\text{1st term}}\underbrace{\left(6.3x^3 + 2.8x^2\right)}_{\text{2nd term}}$

$f'(x) = \underbrace{\left(3.2x^5 - 4.1x^3 + 0.5x\right)}_{\text{1st term}}\underbrace{\left(18.9x^2 + 5.6x\right)}_{\substack{\text{derivative of the} \\ \text{2nd term}}} + \underbrace{\left(6.3x^3 + 2.8x^2\right)}_{\text{2nd term}}\underbrace{\left(16x^4 - 12.3x^2 + 0.5\right)}_{\substack{\text{derivative of the} \\ \text{1st term}}}$

The Quotient Rule

1. Multiply the original denominator by the derivative of the numerator.
2. Subtract the original numerator multiplied by the derivative of the original denominator.
3. Divide the whole expression by the original denominator squared.

6. $f(x) = \dfrac{x^2 + 2}{3x - 5}$

$f'(x) = \dfrac{\overbrace{(3x-5)}^{\text{denominator}}\overbrace{(2x)}^{\substack{\text{derivative of} \\ \text{the numerator}}} - \overbrace{(x^2+2)}^{\text{numerator}}\overbrace{(3)}^{\substack{\text{derivative of} \\ \text{the denominator}}}}{\underbrace{(3x-5)^2}_{\substack{\text{denominator} \\ \text{squared}}}}$

7. $f(x) = \dfrac{x^2 + 5x + 6}{x^4 - x^3}$

$f'(x) = \dfrac{\overbrace{(x^4-x^3)}^{\text{denominator}}\overbrace{(2x+5)}^{\substack{\text{derivative of} \\ \text{the numerator}}} - \overbrace{(x^2+5x+6)}^{\text{numerator}}\overbrace{(4x^3-3x^2)}^{\substack{\text{derivative of} \\ \text{the denominator}}}}{\underbrace{(x^4-x^3)^2}_{\substack{\text{denominator} \\ \text{squared}}}}$

8. $f(x) = \dfrac{\frac{1}{2}x + 8}{x^3 - x}$

$f'(x) = \dfrac{\overbrace{(x^3-x)}^{\text{denominator}}\overbrace{\left(\frac{1}{2}\right)}^{\substack{\text{derivative of} \\ \text{the numerator}}} - \overbrace{\left(\frac{1}{2}x+8\right)}^{\text{numerator}}\overbrace{(3x^2-1)}^{\substack{\text{derivative of} \\ \text{the denominator}}}}{\underbrace{(x^3-x)^2}_{\substack{\text{denominator} \\ \text{squared}}}}$

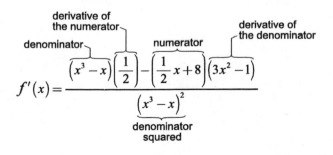

9. $f(x) = \dfrac{3}{x^5 + 6x^4 + 2x}$

$$f'(x) = \frac{\overset{\text{denominator}}{\overbrace{\left(x^5 + 6x^4 + 2x\right)}}\overset{\text{derivative of the numerator}}{(0)} - \overset{\text{numerator}}{3}\overset{\text{derivative of the denominator}}{\left(5x^4 + 24x^3 + 2\right)}}{\underbrace{\left(x^5 + 6x^4 + 2x\right)^2}_{\substack{\text{denominator}\\\text{squared}}}}$$

10. $f(x) = \dfrac{\sqrt{x} + \dfrac{6}{x^3}}{4\sqrt[3]{x}}$

$$f(x) = \frac{x^{\frac{1}{2}} + 6x^{-3}}{4x^{\frac{1}{3}}}$$

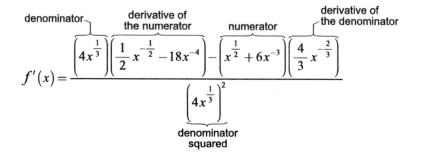

$$f'(x) = \frac{\overset{\text{denominator}}{\overbrace{\left(4x^{\frac{1}{3}}\right)}}\overset{\text{derivative of the numerator}}{\left(\frac{1}{2}x^{-\frac{1}{2}} - 18x^{-4}\right)} - \overset{\text{numerator}}{\overbrace{\left(x^{\frac{1}{2}} + 6x^{-3}\right)}}\overset{\text{derivative of the denominator}}{\left(\frac{4}{3}x^{-\frac{2}{3}}\right)}}{\underbrace{\left(4x^{\frac{1}{3}}\right)^2}_{\substack{\text{denominator}\\\text{squared}}}}$$

The Power Rule

1. Bring the original exponent down and make it a coefficient.
2. Rewrite the original expression to one lower power.
3. Multiply by the derivative of the expression inside the parentheses.

11. $f(x) = \left(x^2 + 4x + 6\right)^3$

$$f'(x) = \underset{\substack{\text{original}\\\text{exponent}}}{3}\underset{\substack{\text{original expression}\\\text{to one lower power}}}{\left(x^2 + 4x + 6\right)^2}\underset{\substack{\text{derivative of the expression}\\\text{inside the parentheses}}}{(2x + 4)}$$

12. $f(x) = \left(5x^3 - x\right)^5$

$$f'(x) = \underset{\substack{\text{original}\\\text{exponent}}}{5}\underset{\substack{\text{original expression}\\\text{to one lower power}}}{\left(5x^3 - x\right)^4}\underset{\substack{\text{derivative of the expression}\\\text{inside the parentheses}}}{\left(15x^2 - 1\right)}$$

13. $f(x) = \sqrt{8x^2 - 11x + 1}$

$f(x) = \left(8x^2 - 11x + 1\right)^{\frac{1}{2}}$

$f'(x) = \underbrace{\frac{1}{2}}_{\substack{\text{original} \\ \text{exponent}}} \underbrace{\left(8x^2 - 11x + 1\right)^{-\frac{1}{2}}}_{\substack{\text{original expression} \\ \text{to one lower power}}} \underbrace{\left(16x - 11\right)}_{\substack{\text{derivative of the expression} \\ \text{inside the parentheses}}}$

14. $f(x) = \dfrac{1}{\left(x^3 + 10x^2\right)^4}$

$f(x) = \left(x^3 + 10x^2\right)^{-4}$

$f'(x) = \underbrace{-4}_{\substack{\text{original} \\ \text{exponent}}} \underbrace{\left(x^3 + 10x^2\right)^{-5}}_{\substack{\text{original expression} \\ \text{to one lower power}}} \underbrace{\left(3x^2 + 20x\right)}_{\substack{\text{derivative of the expression} \\ \text{inside the parentheses}}}$

15. $f(x) = 7\left(x^6 - x^4 + x^2\right)^8$

$f'(x) = \underbrace{8}_{\substack{\text{original} \\ \text{exponent}}}(7)\underbrace{\left(x^6 - x^4 + x^2\right)^7}_{\substack{\text{original expression} \\ \text{to one lower power}}} \underbrace{\left(6x^5 - 4x^3 + 2x\right)}_{\substack{\text{derivative of the expression} \\ \text{inside the parentheses}}}$

DERIVATIVES OF THE SINE, COSINE, AND TANGENT FUNCTIONS

Find the derivatives of each of the following trigonometric functions.

1. $f(x) = \sin x$

2. $f(x) = \cos x$

3. $f(x) = \tan x$

4. $f(x) = \sin 2x$

5. $f(x) = \cos 5x$

6. $f(x) = \tan 3x$

7. $f(x) = 3\sin 6x$

8. $f(x) = \dfrac{1}{2}\cos 4x$

9. $f(x) = \dfrac{\tan 2x}{5}$

10. $f(x) = \sin\left(5x^2 + 3x\right)$

11. $f(x) = \cos\left(x^3 - 8x^2\right)$

12. $f(x) = 2\tan\left(x^4 - \dfrac{1}{2}x + 10\right)$

13. $f(x) = 8\sin\sqrt{x}$

14. $f(x) = \tan\left(\dfrac{2}{x^3}\right)$

15. $f(x) = \cos\left(x^2 + \sqrt[3]{x}\right) - \sin\left(\dfrac{4}{\sqrt{x}}\right)$

Notes

1. $f'(x) = \cos x$

2. $f'(x) = -\sin x$

3. $f'(x) = \sec^2 x$

4. $f'(x) = 2\cos 2x$

5. $f'(x) = -5\sin 5x$

6. $f'(x) = 3\sec^2 3x$

7. $f'(x) = 18\cos 6x$

8. $f'(x) = -2\sin 4x$

9. $f'(x) = \dfrac{2}{5}\sec^2 2x$

10. $f'(x) = (10x+3)\cos(5x^2+3x)$

11. $f'(x) = -(3x^2-16x)\sin(x^3-8x^2)$

12. $f'(x) = 2\left(4x^3 - \dfrac{1}{2}\right)\sec^2\left(x^4 - \dfrac{1}{2}x + 10\right)$

13. $f'(x) = \dfrac{4}{\sqrt{x}}\cos\sqrt{x}$ or $f'(x) = \dfrac{4\sqrt{x}}{x}\cos\sqrt{x}$

14. $f'(x) = -\dfrac{6}{x^4}\sec^2\left(\dfrac{2}{x^3}\right)$

15. $f'(x) = -\left(2x + \dfrac{1}{3\sqrt[3]{x^2}}\right)\sin\left(x^2+\sqrt[3]{x}\right) + \dfrac{2}{x\sqrt{x}}\cos\left(\dfrac{4}{\sqrt{x}}\right)$ or

$f'(x) = -\left(2x + \dfrac{\sqrt[3]{x}}{3x}\right)\sin\left(x^2+\sqrt[3]{x}\right) + \dfrac{2\sqrt{x}}{x^2}\cos\left(\dfrac{4\sqrt{x}}{x}\right)$

Solutions

1. $f(x) = \sin x$

   $f'(x) = \cos x$

2. $f(x) = \cos x$

   $f'(x) = -\sin x$

3. $f(x) = \tan x$

   $f'(x) = \sec^2 x$

4. $f(x) = \sin 2x$

   $f'(x) = 2\cos 2x$

   └ the derivative of $2x$

5. $f(x) = \cos 5x$

   $f'(x) = -5\sin 5x$

   └ the derivative of $5x$

6. $f(x) = \tan 3x$

   $f'(x) = 3\sec^2 3x$

   └ the derivative of $3x$

7. $f(x) = 3\sin 6x$

   $f'(x) = 3(6)\cos 6x$

   └ the derivative of $6x$

   $f'(x) = 18\cos 6x$

8. $f(x) = \dfrac{1}{2}\cos 4x$

   $f'(x) = -\dfrac{1}{2}(4)\sin 4x$

   └ the derivative of $4x$

   $f'(x) = -2\sin 4x$

9. $f(x) = \dfrac{\tan 2x}{5}$

   $f(x) = \dfrac{1}{5}\tan 2x$

   $f'(x) = \dfrac{1}{5}(2)\sec^2 2x$

   └ the derivative of $2x$

   $f'(x) = \dfrac{2}{5}\sec^2 2x$

10. $f(x) = \sin\left(5x^2 + 3x\right)$

$f'(x) = \underbrace{(10x + 3)}_{\substack{\text{the derivative of} \\ 5x^2 + 3x}} \cos\left(5x^2 + 3x\right)$

11. $f(x) = \cos\left(x^3 - 8x^2\right)$

$f'(x) = -\underbrace{\left(3x^2 - 16x\right)}_{\substack{\text{the derivative of} \\ x^3 - 8x^2}} \sin\left(x^3 - 8x^2\right)$

12. $f(x) = 2\tan\left(x^4 - \dfrac{1}{2}x + 10\right)$

$f'(x) = 2\underbrace{\left(4x^3 - \dfrac{1}{2}\right)}_{\substack{\text{the derivative of} \\ x^4 - \frac{1}{2}x + 10}} \sec^2\left(x^4 - \dfrac{1}{2}x + 10\right)$

13. $f(x) = 8\sin\sqrt{x}$

$f(x) = 8\sin x^{\frac{1}{2}}$

$f'(x) = 8\underbrace{\left(\dfrac{1}{2}x^{-\frac{1}{2}}\right)}_{\substack{\text{the derivative of} \\ x^{\frac{1}{2}}}} \cos x^{\frac{1}{2}}$

$f'(x) = \dfrac{4}{x^{\frac{1}{2}}}\cos x^{\frac{1}{2}}$

$f'(x) = \dfrac{4}{\sqrt{x}}\cos\sqrt{x}$

Or, if we wish to rationalize the denominator in the coefficient:

$f'(x) = \dfrac{4}{\sqrt{x}} \cdot \dfrac{\sqrt{x}}{\sqrt{x}}\cos\sqrt{x}$

$f'(x) = \dfrac{4\sqrt{x}}{x}\cos\sqrt{x}$

14. $f(x) = \tan\left(\dfrac{2}{x^3}\right)$

$f(x) = \tan\left(2x^{-3}\right)$

$f'(x) = \underbrace{-6x^{-4}}_{\substack{\text{the derivative of} \\ 2x^{-3}}} \sec^2\left(2x^{-3}\right)$

$f'(x) = -\dfrac{6}{x^4}\sec^2\left(\dfrac{2}{x^3}\right)$

15. $f(x) = \cos\left(x^2 + \sqrt[3]{x}\right) - \sin\left(\dfrac{4}{\sqrt{x}}\right)$

$f(x) = \cos\left(x^2 + x^{\frac{1}{3}}\right) - \sin\left(\dfrac{4}{x^{\frac{1}{2}}}\right)$

$f(x) = \cos\left(x^2 + x^{\frac{1}{3}}\right) - \sin\left(4x^{-\frac{1}{2}}\right)$

Finding the derivative of each term separately, we get:

$f'(x) = -\underbrace{\left(2x + \dfrac{1}{3}x^{-\frac{2}{3}}\right)}_{\substack{\text{the derivative of} \\ x^2 + x^{\frac{1}{3}}}}\sin\left(x^2 + x^{\frac{1}{3}}\right) - \underbrace{\left(-2x^{-\frac{3}{2}}\right)}_{\substack{\text{the derivative of} \\ 4x^{-\frac{1}{2}}}}\cos\left(4x^{-\frac{1}{2}}\right)$

$f'(x) = -\left(2x + \dfrac{1}{3\sqrt[3]{x^2}}\right)\sin\left(x^2 + \sqrt[3]{x}\right) + \dfrac{2}{x\sqrt{x}}\cos\left(\dfrac{4}{\sqrt{x}}\right)$

Or, if we rationalize all denominators:

$f'(x) = -\left(2x + \dfrac{1}{3\sqrt[3]{x^2}} \cdot \dfrac{\sqrt[3]{x}}{\sqrt[3]{x}}\right)\sin\left(x^2 + \sqrt[3]{x}\right) + \dfrac{2}{x\sqrt{x}} \cdot \dfrac{\sqrt{x}}{\sqrt{x}}\cos\left(\dfrac{4}{\sqrt{x}} \cdot \dfrac{\sqrt{x}}{\sqrt{x}}\right)$

$f'(x) = -\left(2x + \dfrac{\sqrt[3]{x}}{3x}\right)\sin\left(x^2 + \sqrt[3]{x}\right) + \dfrac{2\sqrt{x}}{x^2}\cos\left(\dfrac{4\sqrt{x}}{x}\right)$

DERIVATIVES OF TRIGONOMETRIC FUNCTIONS

Calculate the derivative of each of the following trigonometric functions.

1. $f(x) = \sin x$

2. $f(x) = \cos x$

3. $f(x) = \tan x$

4. $f(x) = \sec x$

5. $f(x) = \csc x$

6. $f(x) = \cot x$

7. $f(x) = \sin 5x$

8. $f(x) = \cos 6x$

9. $f(x) = \tan 12x$

10. $f(x) = \sec 9x$

11. $f(x) = \csc 15x$

12. $f(x) = \cot 8x$

13. $y = -5 \sin 2x$

14. $y = \cos(-9x)$

15. $y = \sec(-4x) + \tan x$

16. $y = -\dfrac{1}{5}\cot 10x$

17. $y = -\sin 3x - 4\sin(-5x) - \cos(-3x)$

18. $y = \dfrac{-\csc 2x}{5}$

19. $y = \sec(-2x) - \tan(-2x) + \cot(-x)$

20. $y = \dfrac{\sin 7x}{6} - \dfrac{\cos 5x}{11}$

Answer Key

1. $f'(x) = \cos x$

2. $f'(x) = -\sin x$

3. $f'(x) = \sec^2 x$

4. $f'(x) = \sec x \tan x$

5. $f'(x) = -\csc x \cot x$

6. $f'(x) = -\csc^2 x$

7. $f'(x) = 5\cos 5x$

8. $f'(x) = -6\sin 6x$

9. $f'(x) = 12\sec^2 12x$

10. $f'(x) = 9\sec 9x \tan 9x$

11. $f'(x) = -15\csc x \cot x$

12. $f'(x) = -8\csc^2 8x$

13. $\dfrac{dy}{dx} = -10\cos 2x$

14. $\dfrac{dy}{dx} = 9\sin(-9x)$

15. $\dfrac{dy}{dx} = -4\sec(-4x)\tan(-4x) + \sec^2 x$

16. $\dfrac{dy}{dx} = 2\csc^2 10x$

17. $\dfrac{dy}{dx} = -3\cos 3x + 20\cos(-5x) - 3\sin(-3x)$

18. $\dfrac{dy}{dx} = \dfrac{2}{5}\csc 2x \cot 2x$

19. $\dfrac{dy}{dx} = -2\sec(-2x)\tan(-2x) + 2\sec^2(-2x) + \csc^2(-x)$

20. $\dfrac{dy}{dx} = \dfrac{7}{6}\cos 7x + \dfrac{5}{11}\sin 5x$

Solutions

1. $f(x) = \sin x$

   $f'(x) = \cos x$

2. $f(x) = \cos x$

   $f'(x) = -\sin x$

3. $f(x) = \tan x$

   $f'(x) = \sec^2 x$

4. $f(x) = \sec x$

   $f'(x) = \sec x \tan x$

5. $f(x) = \csc x$

   $f'(x) = -\csc x \cot x$

6. $f(x) = \cot x$

   $f'(x) = -\csc^2 x$

7. $f(x) = \sin 5x$

   $f'(x) = 5 \cos 5x$

8. $f(x) = \cos 6x$

   $f'(x) = -6 \sin 6x$

9. $f(x) = \tan 12x$

   $f'(x) = 12 \sec^2 12x$

10. $f(x) = \sec 9x$

    $f'(x) = 9 \sec 9x \tan 9x$

11. $f(x) = \csc 15x$

    $f'(x) = -15 \csc x \cot x$

12. $f(x) = \cot 8x$

    $f'(x) = -8 \csc^2 8x$

13. $y = -5\sin 2x$

$$\frac{dy}{dx} = -5(2)\cos 2x$$

$$\frac{dy}{dx} = -10\cos 2x$$

14. $y = \cos(-9x)$

$$\frac{dy}{dx} = -(-9)\sin(-9x)$$

$$\frac{dy}{dx} = 9\sin(-9x)$$

15. $y = \sec(-4x) + \tan x$

$$\frac{dy}{dx} = -4\sec(-4x)\tan(-4x) + \sec^2 x$$

16. $y = -\frac{1}{5}\cot 10x$

$$\frac{dy}{dx} = 10\left(-\frac{1}{5}\right)\left(-\csc^2 10x\right)$$

$$\frac{dy}{dx} = 2\csc^2 10x$$

17. $y = -\sin 3x - 4\sin(-5x) - \cos(-3x)$

$$\frac{dy}{dx} = -3\cos 3x - 4(-5)\cos(-5x) + (-3)\sin(-3x)$$

$$\frac{dy}{dx} = -3\cos 3x + 20\cos(-5x) - 3\sin(-3x)$$

18. $y = \dfrac{-\csc 2x}{5}$

$$y = -\frac{1}{5}\csc 2x$$

$$\frac{dy}{dx} = 2\left(-\frac{1}{5}\right)\left(-\csc 2x \cot 2x\right)$$

$$\frac{dy}{dx} = \frac{2}{5}\csc 2x \cot 2x$$

19. $y = \sec(-2x) - \tan(-2x) + \cot(-x)$

$$\frac{dy}{dx} = -2\sec(-2x)\tan(-2x) - (-2)\sec^2(-2x) - \left[-\csc^2(-x)\right]$$

$$\frac{dy}{dx} = -2\sec(-2x)\tan(-2x) + 2\sec^2(-2x) + \csc^2(-x)$$

20. $y = \dfrac{\sin 7x}{6} - \dfrac{\cos 5x}{11}$

$y = \dfrac{1}{6} \sin 7x - \dfrac{1}{11} \cos 5x$

$\dfrac{dy}{dx} = 7\left(\dfrac{1}{6}\right) \cos 7x + 5\left(\dfrac{1}{11}\right) \sin 5x$

$\dfrac{dy}{dx} = \dfrac{7}{6} \cos 7x + \dfrac{5}{11} \sin 5x$

Find the derivative of each of the following.

1. $f(x) = e^{2x}$

2. $f(x) = e^{3x}$

3. $f(x) = e^x$

4. $y = e^{x^2}$

5. $f(x) = e^{x^3 - 6x^2}$

6. $y = 5e^{2x+6}$

7. $f(x) = \dfrac{e^{x^3}}{10}$

8. $y = e^{6.5x + 2.7}$

9. $y = e^{\frac{x^3}{2} - \frac{x}{5}}$

10. $f(x) = e^{\sqrt{x}}$

11. $y = \operatorname{Ln} x^2$

12. $f(x) = \operatorname{Ln}(3x + 6)$

13. $f(x) = \operatorname{Ln} x$

14. $y = \operatorname{Ln}(3x^2 - 5x)$

15. $y = 6\operatorname{Ln}(x - 5)$

16. $f(x) = \operatorname{Ln}\left(\dfrac{x}{6}\right)$

17. $f(x) = \operatorname{Ln}\left(\dfrac{x+5}{x-1}\right)$

18. $f(x) = \operatorname{Ln}(3x^2 - 7x)^4$

19. $y = 8\operatorname{Ln}\left(\dfrac{x^2}{4} - \dfrac{x}{3}\right)$

20. $f(x) = \operatorname{Ln}(x^2 - 3x + 5)(x^3 - 9x)$

Answer Key

1. $f'(x) = 2e^{2x}$

2. $f'(x) = 3e^{3x}$

3. $f'(x) = e^x$

4. $\dfrac{dy}{dx} = 2xe^{x^2}$

5. $f'(x) = \left(3x^2 - 12x\right)e^{x^3 - 6x^2}$

6. $\dfrac{dy}{dx} = 10e^{2x+6}$

7. $f'(x) = \dfrac{1}{10}\left(3x^2\right)e^{x^3}$

8. $\dfrac{dy}{dx} = 6.5\, e^{6.5x + 2.7}$

9. $\dfrac{dy}{dx} = \left(\dfrac{3}{2}x^2 - \dfrac{1}{5}\right)e^{\frac{1}{2}x^3 - \frac{1}{5}x}$

10. $f'(x) = \dfrac{1}{2\sqrt{x}}\, e^{\sqrt{x}}$

11. $\dfrac{dy}{dx} = \dfrac{2}{x}$

12. $f'(x) = \dfrac{1}{x+2}$

13. $f'(x) = \dfrac{1}{x}$

14. $\dfrac{dy}{dx} = \dfrac{6x - 5}{3x^2 - 5x}$

15. $\dfrac{dy}{dx} = \dfrac{6}{x - 5}$

16. $f'(x) = \dfrac{1}{x}$

17. $f'(x) = \dfrac{1}{x+5} - \dfrac{1}{x-1}$

18. $f'(x) = 4\left(\dfrac{6x - 7}{3x^2 - 7x}\right)$

19. $\dfrac{dy}{dx} = 8\left(\dfrac{6x - 4}{3x^2 - 4}\right)$

20. $f'(x) = \dfrac{2x - 3}{x^2 - 3x + 5} + \dfrac{3x^2 - 9}{x^3 - 9x}$

Solutions

1. $f(x) = e^{2x}$

   $f'(x) = 2e^{2x}$

2. $f(x) = e^{3x}$

   $f'(x) = 3e^{3x}$

3. $f(x) = e^x$

   $f'(x) = 1 \cdot e^x$

   $f'(x) = e^x$

4. $y = e^{x^2}$

   $\dfrac{dy}{dx} = 2xe^{x^2}$

5. $f(x) = e^{x^3 - 6x^2}$

   $f'(x) = \left(3x^2 - 12x\right)e^{x^3 - 6x^2}$

6. $y = 5e^{2x+6}$

   $\dfrac{dy}{dx} = 2(5)e^{2x+6}$

   $\dfrac{dy}{dx} = 10e^{2x+6}$

7. $f(x) = \dfrac{e^{x^3}}{10}$

   $f(x) = \dfrac{1}{10}e^{x^3}$

   $f'(x) = \dfrac{1}{10}\left(3x^2\right)e^{x^3}$

8. $y = e^{6.5x+2.7}$

   $\dfrac{dy}{dx} = 6.5\,e^{6.5x+2.7}$

9. $y = e^{\frac{x^3}{2} - \frac{x}{5}}$

   $y = e^{\frac{1}{2}x^3 - \frac{1}{5}x}$

   $\dfrac{dy}{dx} = \left(\dfrac{3}{2}x^2 - \dfrac{1}{5}\right)e^{\frac{1}{2}x^3 - \frac{1}{5}x}$

10. $f(x) = e^{\sqrt{x}}$

    $f(x) = e^{x^{\frac{1}{2}}}$

    $f'(x) = \dfrac{1}{2}x^{-\frac{1}{2}}e^{x^{\frac{1}{2}}}$

    $f'(x) = \dfrac{1}{2\sqrt{x}}e^{\sqrt{x}}$

11. $y = \text{Ln}\,x^2$

    $\dfrac{dy}{dx} = \dfrac{2x}{x^2}$

    $\dfrac{dy}{dx} = \dfrac{2}{x}$

12. $f(x) = \text{Ln}\,(3x+6)$

    $f'(x) = \dfrac{3}{3x+6}$

    $f'(x) = \dfrac{3(1)}{3(x+2)}$

    $f'(x) = \dfrac{1}{x+2}$

13. $f(x) = \text{Ln}\,x$

    $f'(x) = \dfrac{1}{x}$

14. $y = \text{Ln}\,\left(3x^2 - 5x\right)$

    $\dfrac{dy}{dx} = \dfrac{6x-5}{3x^2 - 5x}$

15. $y = 6\,\text{Ln}\,(x-5)$

    $\dfrac{dy}{dx} = 6\left(\dfrac{1}{x-5}\right)$

    $\dfrac{dy}{dx} = \dfrac{6}{x-5}$

16. $f(x) = \text{Ln}\left(\dfrac{x}{6}\right)$

    $f(x) = \text{Ln}\,x - \text{Ln}\,6$

    $f'(x) = \dfrac{1}{x}$

17. $f(x) = \text{Ln}\left(\dfrac{x+5}{x-1}\right)$

$f(x) = \text{Ln}(x+5) - \text{Ln}(x-1)$

$f'(x) = \dfrac{1}{x+5} - \dfrac{1}{x-1}$

18. $f(x) = \text{Ln}(3x^2 - 7x)^4$

$f(x) = 4\,\text{Ln}(3x^2 - 7x)$

$f'(x) = 4\left(\dfrac{6x-7}{3x^2 - 7x}\right)$

19. $y = 8\,\text{Ln}\left(\dfrac{x^2}{4} - \dfrac{x}{3}\right)$

$y = 8\,\text{Ln}\left(\dfrac{3x^2 - 4x}{12}\right)$

$y = 8\,\text{Ln}(3x^2 - 4x) - 8\,\text{Ln}\,12$

$\dfrac{dy}{dx} = 8\left(\dfrac{6x-4}{3x^2 - 4}\right)$

20. $f(x) = \text{Ln}(x^2 - 3x + 5)(x^3 - 9x)$

$f(x) = \text{Ln}(x^2 - 3x + 5) - \text{Ln}(x^3 - 9x)$

$f'(x) = \dfrac{2x-3}{x^2 - 3x + 5} + \dfrac{3x^2 - 9}{x^3 - 9x}$

Find the derivative of each of the following functions.

1. $f(x) = 2^x$

2. $f(x) = 3^x$

3. $f(x) = 5^x$

4. $f(x) = 2^{x^2}$

5. $f(x) = 4^{\sqrt{x}}$

6. $y = 6^{x^3}$

7. $y = 3^{x^4 - 1}$

8. $y = 7^{\sqrt[3]{x} + x}$

9. $y = 8^{\frac{1}{x^2}}$

10. $y = 2^{\frac{5}{\sqrt[4]{x}}}$

11. $f(x) = \log_2 x$

12. $f(x) = \log_7 x$

13. $f(x) = \log_3 x^2$

14. $f(x) = \log_4 (x^3 - 5)$

15. $f(x) = \log_5 \sqrt{x}$

16. $y = \log_6 \left(\sqrt[3]{x} - x^2 \right)$

17. $y = \log_2 \left(\dfrac{1}{x^2} \right)$

18. $y = \log_5 \left(\dfrac{2}{\sqrt{x}} \right)$

19. $y = \text{Log} \left(x^3 - 6x + 2 \right)$

20. $y = \text{Log} \left(\dfrac{1}{x^2} - \dfrac{1}{x^3} \right)$

Answer Key

1. $f'(x) = 2^x \operatorname{Ln} 2$

2. $f'(x) = 3^x \operatorname{Ln} 3$

3. $f'(x) = 5^x \operatorname{Ln} 5$

4. $f'(x) = 2x \cdot 2^{x^2} \operatorname{Ln} 2$

5. $f'(x) = \dfrac{1}{2\sqrt{x}} \cdot 4^{\sqrt{x}} \operatorname{Ln} 4$

6. $\dfrac{dy}{dx} = 3x^2 \cdot 6^{x^3} \operatorname{Ln} 6$

7. $\dfrac{dy}{dx} = 4x^3 \cdot 3^{x^4-1} \operatorname{Ln} 3$

8. $\dfrac{dy}{dx} = \left(\dfrac{1}{3\sqrt[3]{x^2}} + 1 \right) 7^{\sqrt[3]{x}+x} \operatorname{Ln} 7$

9. $\dfrac{dy}{dx} = -\dfrac{2}{x^3} \cdot 8^{\frac{1}{x^2}} \operatorname{Ln} 8$

10. $\dfrac{dy}{dx} = -\dfrac{5}{4x\sqrt[4]{x}} \cdot 2^{\frac{5}{\sqrt[4]{x}}} \operatorname{Ln} 2$

11. $f'(x) = \dfrac{1}{x \operatorname{Ln} 2}$

12. $f'(x) = \dfrac{1}{x \operatorname{Ln} 7}$

13. $f'(x) = \dfrac{2}{x \operatorname{Ln} 3}$

14. $f'(x) = \dfrac{3x^2}{(x^3 - 5) \operatorname{Ln} 4}$

15. $f'(x) = \dfrac{1}{2x \operatorname{Ln} 5}$

16. $\dfrac{dy}{dx} = \dfrac{\dfrac{1}{3\sqrt[3]{x^2}} - 2x}{\left(\sqrt[3]{x} - x^2 \right) \operatorname{Ln} 6}$

17. $\dfrac{dy}{dx} = -\dfrac{2}{x \operatorname{Ln} 2}$

18. $\dfrac{dy}{dx} = -\dfrac{1}{2x \operatorname{Ln} 5}$

19. $\dfrac{dy}{dx} = \dfrac{3x^2 - 6}{\left(x^3 - 6x + 2 \right) \operatorname{Ln} 10}$

20. $\dfrac{dy}{dx} = \dfrac{-\dfrac{2}{x^3} + \dfrac{3}{x^4}}{\left(\dfrac{1}{x^2} - \dfrac{1}{x^3} \right) \operatorname{Ln} 10}$

Solutions

1. $f(x) = 2^x$

   $$f'(x) = \underbrace{(1)}_{\text{the derivative of } x} 2^x \operatorname{Ln} 2 = 2^x \operatorname{Ln} 2$$

2. $f(x) = 3^x$

   $$f'(x) = \underbrace{(1)}_{\text{the derivative of } x} 3^x \operatorname{Ln} 3 = 3^x \operatorname{Ln} 3$$

3. $f(x) = 5^x$

   $$f'(x) = \underbrace{(1)}_{\text{the derivative of } x} 5^x \operatorname{Ln} 5 = 5^x \operatorname{Ln} 5$$

4. $f(x) = 2^{x^2}$

   $$f'(x) = \underbrace{(2x)}_{\text{the derivative of } x^2} 2^{x^2} \operatorname{Ln} 2 = 2x \cdot 2^{x^2} \operatorname{Ln} 2$$

5. $f(x) = 4^{\sqrt{x}}$

   $$f(x) = 4^{x^{\frac{1}{2}}}$$

   $$f'(x) = \underbrace{\left(\frac{1}{2} x^{-\frac{1}{2}} \right)}_{\text{the derivative of } x^{\frac{1}{2}}} 4^{x^{\frac{1}{2}}} \operatorname{Ln} 4 = \frac{1}{2\sqrt{x}} \cdot 4^{\sqrt{x}} \operatorname{Ln} 4$$

6. $y = 6^{x^3}$

   $$\frac{dy}{dx} = \underbrace{3x^2}_{\text{the derivative of } x^3} \cdot 6^{x^3} \operatorname{Ln} 6$$

7. $y = 3^{x^4 - 1}$

   $$\frac{dy}{dx} = \underbrace{4x^3}_{\text{the derivative of } x^4 - 1} \cdot 3^{x^4 - 1} \operatorname{Ln} 3$$

8. $y = 7^{\sqrt[3]{x} + x}$

   $$y = 7^{x^{\frac{1}{3}} + x}$$

   $$\frac{dy}{dx} = \underbrace{\left(\frac{1}{3} x^{-\frac{2}{3}} + 1 \right)}_{\text{the derivative of } x^{\frac{1}{3}} + x} 7^{x^{\frac{1}{3}} + x} \operatorname{Ln} 7 = \left(\frac{1}{3\sqrt[3]{x^2}} + 1 \right) 7^{\sqrt[3]{x} + x} \operatorname{Ln} 7$$

9. $y = 8^{\frac{1}{x^2}}$

$y = 8^{x^{-2}}$

$$\frac{dy}{dx} = \underbrace{-2x^{-3}}_{\text{the derivative of } x^{-2}} \cdot 8^{x^{-2}} \operatorname{Ln} 8 = -\frac{2}{x^3} \cdot 8^{\frac{1}{x^2}} \operatorname{Ln} 8$$

10. $y = 2^{\frac{5}{\sqrt[4]{x}}}$

$y = 2^{5x^{-\frac{1}{4}}}$

$$\frac{dy}{dx} = \underbrace{\left[5\left(-\frac{1}{4}\right)x^{-\frac{5}{4}}\right]}_{\text{the derivative of } 5x^{-\frac{1}{4}}} 2^{5x^{-\frac{1}{4}}} \operatorname{Ln} 2 = -\frac{5}{4x\sqrt[4]{x}} \cdot 2^{\frac{5}{\sqrt[4]{x}}} \operatorname{Ln} 2$$

11. $f(x) = \log_2 x$

$$f'(x) = \frac{1}{x \operatorname{Ln} 2} \cdot \underbrace{1}_{\text{the derivative of } x} = \frac{1}{x \operatorname{Ln} 2}$$

12. $f(x) = \log_7 x$

$$f'(x) = \frac{1}{x \operatorname{Ln} 7} \cdot \underbrace{1}_{\text{the derivative of } x} = \frac{1}{x \operatorname{Ln} 7}$$

13. $f(x) = \log_3 x^2$

$$f'(x) = \frac{1}{x^2 \operatorname{Ln} 3} \cdot \underbrace{2x}_{\text{the derivative of } x^2} = \frac{2x}{x^2 \operatorname{Ln} 3} = \frac{2}{x \operatorname{Ln} 3}$$

14. $f(x) = \log_4\left(x^3 - 5\right)$

$$f'(x) = \frac{1}{\left(x^3 - 5\right)\operatorname{Ln} 4} \cdot \underbrace{3x^2}_{\text{the derivative of } x^3 - 5} = \frac{3x^2}{\left(x^3 - 5\right)\operatorname{Ln} 4}$$

15. $f(x) = \log_5 \sqrt{x}$

$f(x) = \log_5 x^{\frac{1}{2}}$

$$f'(x) = \frac{1}{x^{\frac{1}{2}} \operatorname{Ln} 5} \cdot \underbrace{\frac{1}{2}x^{-\frac{1}{2}}}_{\text{the derivative of } x^{\frac{1}{2}}} = \frac{1}{2x^{\frac{1}{2}} \cdot x^{\frac{1}{2}} \operatorname{Ln} 5} = \frac{1}{2x \operatorname{Ln} 5}$$

16. $y = \log_6\left(\sqrt[3]{x} - x^2\right)$

$y = \log_6\left(x^{\frac{1}{3}} - x^2\right)$

$$\frac{dy}{dx} = \frac{1}{\left(x^{\frac{1}{3}} - x^2\right)\text{Ln }6}\underbrace{\left(\frac{1}{3}x^{-\frac{2}{3}} - 2x\right)}_{\text{the derivative of } x^{\frac{1}{3}} - x^2} = \frac{\dfrac{1}{3\sqrt[3]{x^2}} - 2x}{\left(\sqrt[3]{x} - x^2\right)\text{Ln }6}$$

17. $y = \log_2\left(\dfrac{1}{x^2}\right)$

$y = \log_2 x^{-2}$

$$\frac{dy}{dx} = \frac{1}{x^{-2}\,\text{Ln }2}\underbrace{\left(-2x^{-3}\right)}_{\text{the derivative of } x^{-2}} = -\frac{2}{x\,\text{Ln }2}$$

18. $y = \log_5\left(\dfrac{2}{\sqrt{x}}\right)$

$y = \log_5 2x^{-\frac{1}{2}}$

$$\frac{dy}{dx} = \frac{1}{2x^{-\frac{1}{2}}\,\text{Ln }5}\underbrace{\left(-x^{-\frac{3}{2}}\right)}_{\text{the derivative of } 2x^{-\frac{1}{2}}} = -\frac{1}{2x^{\frac{3}{2}}\cdot x^{-\frac{1}{2}}\,\text{Ln }5} = -\frac{1}{2x\,\text{Ln }5}$$

19. $y = \text{Log}\left(x^3 - 6x + 2\right)$

Since the expression Log with a capital "L" has an implied base of 10:

$y = \text{Log}\left(x^3 - 6x + 2\right) = \log_{10}\left(x^3 - 6x + 2\right)$

$$\frac{dy}{dx} = \frac{1}{\left(x^3 - 6x + 2\right)\text{Ln }10}\underbrace{\left(3x^2 - 6\right)}_{\text{the derivative of } x^3 - 6x + 2} = \frac{3x^2 - 6}{\left(x^3 - 6x + 2\right)\text{Ln }10}$$

20. $y = \text{Log}\left(\dfrac{1}{x^2} - \dfrac{1}{x^3}\right)$

Since the expression Log with a capital "L" has an implied base of 10:

$$y = \text{Log}\left(\frac{1}{x^2} - \frac{1}{x^3}\right) = \log_{10}\left(x^{-2} - x^{-3}\right)$$

$$\frac{dy}{dx} = \frac{1}{\left(x^{-2} - x^{-3}\right)\text{Ln}\,10}\underbrace{\left(-2x^{-3} + 3x^{-4}\right)}_{\text{the derivative of } x^{-2} - x^{-3}} = \frac{-\dfrac{2}{x^3} + \dfrac{3}{x^4}}{\left(\dfrac{1}{x^2} - \dfrac{1}{x^3}\right)\text{Ln}\,10}$$

PRODUCT RULE, QUOTIENT RULE, AND POWER RULE II: ADVANCED FUNCTIONS

Use the Power Rule to find the derivative of each of the following.

1. $f(x) = \left(x^2 + e^{3x}\right)^5$

2. $y = \left(\sin 5x + \cos 2x\right)^4$

3. $f(x) = \left[\operatorname{Ln} x^3 + \tan\left(2x - 1\right)\right]^3$

4. $y = \sqrt{e^{x^2} + \log_3 x}$

5. $y = \dfrac{3}{\sqrt[4]{x^5 - 2^x}}$

Use the Product Rule to find the derivative of each of the following.

6. $f(x) = \left(x^2 + 5x\right)\left(2x + e^{9x-1}\right)$

7. $y = \left[\operatorname{Ln}\left(x^2 - 9x\right) + 7x\right]\left(6^x - x^3\right)$

8. $f(x) = \left(\sin 6x^2 + \cos 2x\right)\left(\tan 5x - 10x^4\right)$

9. $y = \left(e^{-x} + 2x^5\right)\left[-\sin\left(x^3 - 8x\right) + \log_8 x\right]$

10. $f(x) = \left[7\cos\left(x^5 - 4x^3 + 2\right) + \sqrt{x}\right]\left[\tan 4x^3 - \operatorname{Ln}\left(x^7 - 5x^2\right)\right]$

Use the Quotient Rule to find the derivative of each of the following.

11. $y = \dfrac{e^{6x} + x^2}{3x + \sin x}$

12. $f(x) = \dfrac{\tan\left(5x - 1\right) + \operatorname{Ln}\left(7x^2 - 4x + 2\right)}{\cos\left(2x - 6\right) + x^5}$

13. $y = \dfrac{10^x + e^{5x} + 6}{\operatorname{Ln} 7x}$

14. $f(x) = \dfrac{\sqrt[3]{x} - \log_6 x}{\tan\left(2x^3 + x^2 + 5x\right)}$

15. $f(x) = \dfrac{8\sin 7x - 5e^{x^2 - x - 1}}{\operatorname{Ln}\left(12x^2 + 10x\right) + 3.4}$

Solutions

* Note: Some of the solutions in this section have intentionally been left unsimplified so that you can check the solutions term by term.

1. $f(x) = \left(x^2 + e^{3x}\right)^5$

   $f'(x) = 5\left(x^2 + e^{3x}\right)^4 \left(2x + 3e^{3x}\right)$

2. $y = \left(\sin 5x + \cos 2x\right)^4$

   $\dfrac{dy}{dx} = 4\left(\sin 5x + \cos 2x\right)^3 \left(5\cos 5x - 2\sin 2x\right)$

3. $f(x) = \left[\operatorname{Ln} x^3 + \tan\left(2x - 1\right)\right]^3$

   $f'(x) = 3\left[\operatorname{Ln} x^3 + \tan\left(2x - 1\right)\right]^2 \left[\dfrac{3x^2}{x^3} + 2\sec^2\left(2x - 1\right)\right]$

   $f'(x) = 3\left[\operatorname{Ln} x^3 + \tan\left(2x - 1\right)\right]^2 \left[\dfrac{3}{x} + 2\sec^2\left(2x - 1\right)\right]$

4. $y = \sqrt{e^{x^2} + \log_3 x}$

   $y = \left(e^{x^2} + \log_3 x\right)^{\frac{1}{2}}$

   $\dfrac{dy}{dx} = \dfrac{1}{2}\left(e^{x^2} + \log_3 x\right)^{-\frac{1}{2}}\left(2xe^{x^2} + \dfrac{1}{\operatorname{Ln} 3}\cdot\dfrac{1}{x}\right)$

   $\dfrac{dy}{dx} = \dfrac{2xe^{x^2} + \dfrac{1}{x\operatorname{Ln} 3}}{2\left(e^{x^2} + \log_3 x\right)^{\frac{1}{2}}}$

   $\dfrac{dy}{dx} = \dfrac{2xe^{x^2} + \dfrac{1}{x\operatorname{Ln} 3}}{2\sqrt{e^{x^2} + \log_3 x}}$

5. $y = \dfrac{3}{\sqrt[4]{x^5 - 2^x}}$

$y = \dfrac{3}{\left(x^5 - 2^x\right)^{\frac{1}{4}}}$

$y = 3\left(x^5 - 2^x\right)^{-\frac{1}{4}}$

$\dfrac{dy}{dx} = -\dfrac{1}{4}(3)\left(x^5 - 2^x\right)^{-\frac{5}{4}}\left[5x^4 - (Ln\,2)2^x\right]$

$\dfrac{dy}{dx} = -\dfrac{3}{4}\left(x^5 - 2^x\right)^{-\frac{5}{4}}\left[5x^4 - (Ln\,2)2^x\right]$

$\dfrac{dy}{dx} = -\dfrac{3\left[5x^4 - (Ln\,2)2^x\right]}{4\left(x^5 - 2^x\right)^{\frac{5}{4}}}$

$\dfrac{dy}{dx} = -\dfrac{3\left[5x^4 - (Ln\,2)2^x\right]}{4\left(x^5 - 2^x\right)\sqrt[4]{x^5 - 2^x}}$

6. $f(x) = \left(x^2 + 5x\right)\left(2x + e^{9x-1}\right)$

$f'(x) = \left(x^2 + 5x\right)\left(2 + 9e^{9x-1}\right) + \left(2x + e^{9x-1}\right)(2x + 5)$

7. $y = \left[Ln\left(x^2 - 9x\right) + 7x\right]\left(6^x - x^3\right)$

$\dfrac{dy}{dx} = \left[Ln\left(x^2 - 9x\right) + 7x\right]\left[(Ln\,6)6^x - 3x^2\right] + \left(6^x - x^3\right)\left(\dfrac{2x - 9}{x^2 - 9x} + 7\right)$

8. $f(x) = \left(\sin 6x^2 + \cos 2x\right)\left(\tan 5x - 10x^4\right)$

$f'(x) = \left(\sin 6x^2 + \cos 2x\right)\left(5\sec^2 5x - 40x^3\right) + \left(\tan 5x - 10x^4\right)\left(12x\cos 6x^2 - 2\sin 2x\right)$

9. $y = \left(e^{-x} + 2x^5\right)\left[-\sin\left(x^3 - 8x\right) + \log_8 x\right]$

$\dfrac{dy}{dx} = \left(e^{-x} + 2x^5\right)\left[-\left(3x^2 - 8\right)\cos\left(x^3 - 8x\right) + \dfrac{1}{Ln\,8} \cdot \dfrac{1}{x}\right] + \left[-\sin\left(x^3 - 8x\right) + \log_8 x\right]\left(-e^{-x} + 10x^4\right)$

10. $f(x) = \left[7\cos\left(x^5 - 4x^3 + 2\right) + \sqrt{x}\right]\left[\tan 4x^3 - Ln\left(x^7 - 5x^2\right)\right]$

$f(x) = \left[7\cos\left(x^5 - 4x^3 + 2\right) + x^{\frac{1}{2}}\right]\left[\tan 4x^3 - Ln\left(x^7 - 5x^2\right)\right]$

$f'(x) = \left[7\cos\left(x^5 - 4x^3 + 2\right) + x^{\frac{1}{2}}\right]\left[12x^2 \sec^2 4x^3 - \dfrac{7x^6 - 10x}{x^7 - 5x^2}\right]$

$\qquad + \left[\tan 4x^3 - Ln\left(x^7 - 5x^2\right)\right]\left[-7\left(5x^4 - 12x^3\right)\sin\left(x^5 - 4x^3 + 2\right) + \dfrac{1}{2}x^{-\frac{1}{2}}\right]$

11. $y = \dfrac{e^{6x} + x^2}{3x + \sin x}$

$$\frac{dy}{dx} = \frac{(3x + \sin x)(6e^{6x} + 2x) - (e^{6x} + x^2)(3 + \cos x)}{(3x + \sin x)^2}$$

12. $f(x) = \dfrac{\tan(5x - 1) + \operatorname{Ln}(7x^2 - 4x + 2)}{\cos(2x - 6) + x^5}$

$$f'(x) = \frac{\left[\cos(2x - 6) + 5x^4\right]\left[5\sec^2(5x - 1) + \dfrac{14x - 4}{7x^2 - 4x + 2}\right] - \left[\tan(5x - 1) + \operatorname{Ln}(7x^2 - 4x + 2)\right]\left[-2\sin(2x - 6) + 5x^4\right]}{\left[\cos(2x - 6) + x^5\right]^2}$$

13. $y = \dfrac{10^x + e^{5x} + 6}{\operatorname{Ln} 7x}$

$$\frac{dy}{dx} = \frac{\operatorname{Ln} 7x\left[(\operatorname{Ln} 10)10^x + 5e^{5x}\right] - (10^x + e^{5x} + 6)\left(\dfrac{7}{7x}\right)}{(\operatorname{Ln} 7x)^2}$$

14. $f(x) = \dfrac{\sqrt[3]{x} - \log_6 x}{\tan(2x^3 + x^2 + 5x)}$

$$f(x) = \frac{x^{\frac{1}{3}} - \log_6 x}{\tan(2x^3 + x^2 + 5x)}$$

$$f'(x) = \frac{\left[\tan(2x^3 + x^2 + 5x)\right]\left(\dfrac{1}{3}x^{-\frac{2}{3}} - \dfrac{1}{\operatorname{Ln} 6}\cdot\dfrac{1}{x}\right) - \left[x^{\frac{1}{3}} - \log_6 x\right]\left[(6x^2 + 2x + 5)\sec^2(2x^3 + x^2 + 5x)\right]}{\tan^2(2x^3 + x^2 + 5x)}$$

15. $f(x) = \dfrac{8\sin 7x - 5e^{x^2 - x - 1}}{\operatorname{Ln}(12x^2 + 10x) + 3.4}$

$$f'(x) = \frac{\left[\operatorname{Ln}(12x^2 + 10x) + 3.4\right]\left[56\cos 7x - 5(2x - 1)e^{x^2 - x - 1}\right] - \left(8\sin 7x - 5e^{x^2 - x - 1}\right)\left(\dfrac{24x + 10}{12x^2 + 10}\right)}{\left[\operatorname{Ln}(12x^2 + 10x) + 3.4\right]^2}$$

DERIVATIVE
SUMMARY

Find the derivative of each of the following.

1. $f(x) = x^2$

2. $f(x) = x^3 - \dfrac{1}{2}x$

3. $y = (3x + 5)^6$

4. $y = \sin(7x^2 + 3x + 2)$

5. $f(x) = \cos(-x^5 + x^3 - x)$

6. $y = e^{4x^6}$

7. $f(x) = \operatorname{Ln}(8x^3 - 5x^2)$

8. $f(x) = \sqrt{x + 2}$

9. $f(x) = \dfrac{10}{\sqrt[3]{x}}$

10. $y = 12^x$

11. $y = (6x^2 + 3x + 10)(7x^4 - 9x^2)$

12. $y = \log_5 x$

13. $f(x) = \tan(x^3 - 8x)$

14. $f(x) = \dfrac{x^2 + 6x - 5}{x^3 + 9x^2}$

15. $f(x) = e^{2x} + \sin 10x$

16. $y = \left[\operatorname{Ln}(6x^2 + 5x) + (\cos 4x)\right]^5$

17. $f(x) = 2.7$

18. $f(x) = (x^2 + 7x)(x^3 - 3x)^4$

19. $y = \sqrt{\dfrac{e^{2x}}{\tan(x^5 + 12x)}}$

20. $y = \dfrac{\sin(6x - 1) + (5x^2 - 2x)^3 + \operatorname{Ln}(3x^2 + 8x)}{e^{\sqrt{x}} + \dfrac{1}{x^9}}$

Answer Key

1. $2x$

2. $3x^2 - \dfrac{1}{2}$

3. $18(3x+5)^5$

4. $(14x+3)\cos(7x^2+3x+2)$

5. $(5x^4-3x^2+1)\sin(-x^5+x^3-x)$

6. $24x^5 e^{4x^6}$

7. $\dfrac{24x^2-10x}{8x^3-5x^2}$

8. $\dfrac{1}{2\sqrt{x+2}}$

9. $-\dfrac{10}{3x\sqrt[3]{x}}$

10. $(\text{Ln}\,12)12^x$

11. $(6x^2+3x+10)(28x^3-18x)+(7x^4-9x^2)(12x+3)$

12. $\dfrac{1}{\text{Ln}\,5}\cdot\dfrac{1}{x}$

13. $(3x^2-8)\sec^2(x^3-8x)$

14. $\dfrac{(x^3+9x^2)(2x+6)-(x^2+6x-5)(3x^2+18x)}{(x^3+9x^2)^2}$

15. $2e^{2x}+10\cos 10x$

16. $5\big[\text{Ln}(6x^2+5x)+\cos 4x\big]^4\left(\dfrac{12x+5}{6x^2+5x}-4\sin 4x\right)$

17. 0

18. $(x^2+7x)\big[4(x^3-3x)^3(3x^2-3)\big]+(x^3-3x)^4(2x+7)$

19. $\dfrac{1}{2}\left[\dfrac{e^{2x}}{\tan(x^5+12x)}\right]^{-\frac{1}{2}}\left[\dfrac{\tan(x^5+12x)\cdot 2e^{2x}-e^{2x}(5x^4+12)\sec^2(x^5+12x)}{\tan^2(x^5+12x)}\right]$

20. $\dfrac{\left(e^{x^{\frac{1}{2}}}+x^{-9}\right)\left[6\cos(6x-1)+3(5x^2-2x)^2(10x-2)+\dfrac{6x+8}{3x^2+8x}\right]-\left[\sin(6x-1)+(5x^2-2x)^3+\text{Ln}(3x^2+8x)\right]\left(\dfrac{1}{2}x^{-\frac{1}{2}}e^{x^{\frac{1}{2}}}-9x^{-10}\right)}{\left(e^{x^{\frac{1}{2}}}+x^{-9}\right)^2}$

Solutions

* Note: In this section some of the solutions have intentionally been left unsimplified so that you may check the answer term by term.

1. $f(x) = x^2$

   $f'(x) = 2x$

2. $f(x) = x^3 - \dfrac{1}{2}x$

   $f'(x) = 3x^2 - \dfrac{1}{2}$

3. $y = (3x + 5)^6$

   $\dfrac{dy}{dx} = 6(3x + 5)^5(3)$

   $\dfrac{dy}{dx} = 18(3x + 5)^5$

4. $y = \sin(7x^2 + 3x + 2)$

   $\dfrac{dy}{dx} = (14x + 3)\cos(7x^2 + 3x + 2)$

5. $f(x) = \cos(-x^5 + x^3 - x)$

   $f'(x) = -(-5x^4 + 3x^2 - 1)\sin(-x^5 + x^3 - x)$

   $f'(x) = (5x^4 - 3x^2 + 1)\sin(-x^5 + x^3 - x)$

6. $y = e^{4x^6}$

   $\dfrac{dy}{dx} = 24x^5 e^{4x^6}$

7. $f(x) = \operatorname{Ln}(8x^3 - 5x^2)$

   $f'(x) = \dfrac{24x^2 - 10x}{8x^3 - 5x^2}$

8. $f(x) = \sqrt{x + 2}$

   $f(x) = (x + 2)^{\frac{1}{2}}$

   $f'(x) = \dfrac{1}{2}(x + 2)^{-\frac{1}{2}}$

   $f'(x) = \dfrac{1}{2(x + 2)^{\frac{1}{2}}}$

   $f'(x) = \dfrac{1}{2\sqrt{x + 2}}$

9. $f(x) = \dfrac{10}{\sqrt[3]{x}}$

   $f(x) = \dfrac{10}{x^{\frac{1}{3}}}$

   $f(x) = 10x^{-\frac{1}{3}}$

   $f'(x) = -\dfrac{1}{3}(10)x^{-\frac{4}{3}}$

   $f'(x) = -\dfrac{10}{3}x^{-\frac{4}{3}}$

   $f'(x) = -\dfrac{10}{3x^{\frac{4}{3}}}$

   $f'(x) = -\dfrac{10}{3x\sqrt[3]{x}}$

10. $y = 12^x$

    $\dfrac{dy}{dx} = (\operatorname{Ln}12)12^x$

11. $y = \left(6x^2 + 3x + 10\right)\left(7x^4 - 9x^2\right)$

Using the Product Rule:

$$\frac{dy}{dx} = \left(6x^2 + 3x + 10\right)\left(28x^3 - 18x\right) + \left(7x^4 - 9x^2\right)\left(12x + 3\right)$$

12. $y = \log_5 x$

$$\frac{dy}{dx} = \frac{1}{\mathrm{Ln}\, 5} \cdot \frac{1}{x}$$

13. $f(x) = \tan\left(x^3 - 8x\right)$

$$f'(x) = \left(3x^2 - 8\right)\sec^2\left(x^3 - 8x\right)$$

14. $f(x) = \dfrac{x^2 + 6x - 5}{x^3 + 9x^2}$

Using the Quotient Rule:

$$f'(x) = \frac{\left(x^3 + 9x^2\right)\left(2x + 6\right) - \left(x^2 + 6x - 5\right)\left(3x^2 + 18x\right)}{\left(x^3 + 9x^2\right)^2}$$

15. $f(x) = e^{2x} + \sin 10x$

$$f'(x) = 2e^{2x} + 10\cos 10x$$

16. $y = \left[\mathrm{Ln}\left(6x^2 + 5x\right) + \left(\cos 4x\right)\right]^5$

We begin with the Power Rule. To find the derivatives of the terms inside the brackets, we use the individual rules for the natural log and cosine functions.

$$\frac{dy}{dx} = 5\left[\mathrm{Ln}\left(6x^2 + 5x\right) + \cos 4x\right]^4 \left(\frac{12x + 5}{6x^2 + 5x} - 4\sin 4x\right)$$

17. $f(x) = 2.7$

$$f'(x) = 0$$

18. $f(x) = \left(x^2 + 7x\right)\left(x^3 - 3x\right)^4$

We begin with the Product Rule. When taking the derivative of the second term we employ the Power Rule.

$$f'(x) = \left(x^2 + 7x\right)\left[4\left(x^3 - 3x\right)^3\left(3x^2 - 3\right)\right] + \left(x^3 - 3x\right)^4\left(2x + 7\right)$$

19. $y = \sqrt{\dfrac{e^{2x}}{\tan\left(x^5 + 12x\right)}}$

$y = \left[\dfrac{e^{2x}}{\tan\left(x^5 + 12x\right)}\right]^{\frac{1}{2}}$

To find the derivative we use the Power Rule. When finding the derivative of the expression inside the brackets we use both the Quotient Rule and the individual rules for the exponential and tangent functions.

$$\dfrac{dy}{dx} = \dfrac{1}{2}\left[\dfrac{e^{2x}}{\tan\left(x^5 + 12x\right)}\right]^{-\frac{1}{2}}\left[\dfrac{\tan\left(x^5 + 12x\right) \cdot 2e^{2x} - e^{2x}\left(5x^4 + 12\right)\sec^2\left(x^5 + 12x\right)}{\tan^2\left(x^5 + 12x\right)}\right]$$

20. $y = \dfrac{\sin\left(6x - 1\right) + \left(5x^2 - 2x\right)^3 + \operatorname{Ln}\left(3x^2 + 8x\right)}{e^{\sqrt{x}} + \dfrac{1}{x^9}}$

$y = \dfrac{\sin\left(6x - 1\right) + \left(5x^2 - 2x\right)^3 + \operatorname{Ln}\left(3x^2 + 8x\right)}{e^{x^{\frac{1}{2}}} + x^{-9}}$

Using the Quotient Rule as the overall rule to find the derivative:

$$\dfrac{dy}{dx} = \dfrac{\left(e^{x^{\frac{1}{2}}} + x^{-9}\right)\left[6\cos\left(6x - 1\right) + 3\left(5x^2 - 2x\right)^2\left(10x - 2\right) + \dfrac{6x + 8}{3x^2 + 8x}\right] - \left[\sin\left(6x - 1\right) + \left(5x^2 - 2x\right)^3 + \operatorname{Ln}\left(3x^2 + 8x\right)\right]\left(\dfrac{1}{2}x^{-\frac{1}{2}}e^{x^{\frac{1}{2}}} - 9x^{-10}\right)}{\left(e^{x^{\frac{1}{2}}} + x^{-9}\right)^2}$$

Find the differential element dy for each of the following.

1. $y = x^2 + 3x$

2. $y = \left(4x^3 + 6x\right)\left(7x - 1\right)$

3. $y = \left(x^3 - x^2 - x - 6\right)^5$

4. $y = e^{x^3}$

5. $y = \operatorname{Ln}\left(x^2 - x + 2\right)$

6. $y = \sin 10x$

7. $y = \tan\left(9x^2 + 7x\right)$

8. $y = \sqrt[3]{x}$

9. $y = 2^{x^2}$

10. $y = \cos 4x + \dfrac{x+1}{7x^2 + 5}$

Answer Key

1. $dy = (2x + 3)\, dx$

2. $dy = \left[(4x^3 + 6x)(7) + (7x - 1)(12^2 + 6)\right] dx$

3. $dy = 5(x^3 - x^2 - x - 6)^4 (3x^2 - 2x - 1)\, dx$

4. $dy = 3x^2 e^{x^3}\, dx$

5. $dy = \left(\dfrac{2x - 1}{x^2 - x + 2}\right) dx$

6. $dy = (10 \cos 10x)\, dx$

7. $dy = \left[(18x + 7)\sec^2 (9x^2 + 7x)\right] dx$

8. $dy = \left(\dfrac{1}{3\sqrt[3]{x^2}}\right) dx$

9. $dy = \left(2x \cdot \text{Ln}\, 2 \cdot 2^{x^2}\right) dx$

10. $dy = \left[-4\sin 4x + \dfrac{-7x^2 - 14x + 5}{\left(7x^2 + 5\right)^2}\right] dx$

Solutions

1. $y = x^2 + 3x$

    $$\frac{dy}{dx} = 2x + 3$$

    $$\frac{dy}{dx} \cdot dx = (2x + 3) \, dx$$

    $\Rightarrow dy = (2x + 3) \, dx$

2. $y = (4x^3 + 6x)(7x - 1)$

    Using the Product Rule:

    $$\frac{dy}{dx} = (4x^3 + 6x)(7) + (7x - 1)(12^2 + 6)$$

    $$\frac{dy}{dx} \cdot dx = \left[(4x^3 + 6x)(7) + (7x - 1)(12^2 + 6) \right] dx$$

    $\Rightarrow dy = \left[(4x^3 + 6x)(7) + (7x - 1)(12^2 + 6) \right] dx$

3. $y = (x^3 - x^2 - x - 6)^5$

    Using the Power Rule:

    $$\frac{dy}{dx} = 5(x^3 - x^2 - x - 6)^4 (3x^2 - 2x - 1)$$

    $$\frac{dy}{dx} \cdot dx = \left[5(x^3 - x^2 - x - 6)^4 (3x^2 - 2x - 1) \right] dx$$

    $\Rightarrow dy = 5(x^3 - x^2 - x - 6)^4 (3x^2 - 2x - 1) \, dx$

4. $y = e^{x^3}$

    $$\frac{dy}{dx} = 3x^2 e^{x^3}$$

    $$\frac{dy}{dx} \cdot dx = \left(3x^2 e^{x^3} \right) dx$$

    $\Rightarrow dy = 3x^2 e^{x^3} \, dx$

5. $y = \text{Ln}\left(x^2 - x + 2\right)$

$$\frac{dy}{dx} = \frac{2x - 1}{x^2 - x + 2}$$

$$\frac{dy}{dx} \cdot dx = \left(\frac{2x - 1}{x^2 - x + 2}\right) dx$$

$$\Rightarrow \quad dy = \left(\frac{2x - 1}{x^2 - x + 2}\right) dx$$

6. $y = \sin 10$

$$\frac{dy}{dx} = 10 \cos 10x$$

$$\frac{dy}{dx} \cdot dx = \left(10 \cos 10x\right) dx$$

$$\Rightarrow \quad dy = \left(10 \cos 10x\right) dx$$

7. $y = \tan\left(9x^2 + 7x\right)$

$$\frac{dy}{dx} = \left(18x + 7\right) \sec^2\left(9x^2 + 7x\right)$$

$$\frac{dy}{dx} \cdot dx = \left[\left(18x + 7\right) \sec^2\left(9x^2 + 7x\right)\right] dx$$

$$\Rightarrow \quad dy = \left[\left(18x + 7\right) \sec^2\left(9x^2 + 7x\right)\right] dx$$

8. $y = \sqrt[3]{x}$

$$y = x^{\frac{1}{3}}$$

$$\frac{dy}{dx} = \frac{1}{3} x^{-\frac{2}{3}}$$

$$\frac{dy}{dx} = \frac{1}{3x^{\frac{2}{3}}}$$

$$\frac{dy}{dx} = \frac{1}{3\sqrt[3]{x^2}}$$

$$\frac{dy}{dx} \cdot dx = \left(\frac{1}{3\sqrt[3]{x^2}}\right) dx$$

$$\Rightarrow \quad dy = \left(\frac{1}{3\sqrt[3]{x^2}}\right) dx$$

9. $y = 2^{x^2}$

$$\frac{dy}{dx} = 2x \cdot \text{Ln } 2 \cdot 2^{x^2}$$

$$\frac{dy}{dx} \cdot dx = \left(2x \cdot \text{Ln } 2 \cdot 2^{x^2} \right) dx$$

$$\Rightarrow dy = \left(2x \cdot \text{Ln } 2 \cdot 2^{x^2} \right) dx$$

10. $y = \cos 4x + \dfrac{x+1}{7x^2 + 5}$

Using the Quotient Rule of the 2nd term:

$$\frac{dy}{dx} = -4 \sin 4x + \frac{\left(7x^2 + 5\right)(1) - (x+1)(14x)}{\left(7x^2 + 5\right)^2}$$

$$\frac{dy}{dx} = -4 \sin 4x + \frac{7x^2 + 5 - (x+1)(14x)}{\left(7x^2 + 5\right)^2}$$

$$\frac{dy}{dx} = -4 \sin 4x + \frac{7x^2 + 5 - 14x^2 - 14x}{\left(7x^2 + 5\right)^2}$$

$$\frac{dy}{dx} = -4 \sin 4x + \frac{-7x^2 - 14x + 5}{\left(7x^2 + 5\right)^2}$$

$$\frac{dy}{dx} \cdot dx = \left[-4 \sin 4x + \frac{-7x^2 - 14x + 5}{\left(7x^2 + 5\right)^2} \right] dx$$

$$\Rightarrow dy = \left[-4 \sin 4x + \frac{-7x^2 - 14x + 5}{\left(7x^2 + 5\right)^2} \right] dx$$

THE
CHAIN RULE

Find $\dfrac{dy}{du}$, $\dfrac{du}{dx}$, and $\dfrac{dy}{dx}$.

1. $y = u^3$ $u = 2x + 1$

2. $y = u^2 + 3u$ $u = x^2 - 3$

3. $y = \sqrt{u}$ $u = x^4 + 5x^2 + 3$

4. $y = \dfrac{1}{u^5}$ $u = \sqrt[3]{x}$

5. $y = e^{4u}$ $u = x^3 + 7x$

6. $y = \sin 8u$ $u = \cos 12x$

7. $y = \text{Ln}\left(5u^2 + 9u\right)$ $u = x^2 + 3x$

8. $y = 3^{u^2}$ $u = x - 1$

9. $y = \tan\left(u^2 - 8u\right)$ $u = \dfrac{1}{x}$

10. $y = \log_2 u^3$ $u = \dfrac{2}{\sqrt{x}}$

Answer Key

1. $\dfrac{dy}{du} = 3u^2$

    $\dfrac{du}{dx} = 2$

    $\dfrac{dy}{dx} = 6u^2$

2. $\dfrac{dy}{du} = 2u + 3$

    $\dfrac{du}{dx} = 2x$

    $\dfrac{dy}{dx} = 4x^2 - 6x$

3. $\dfrac{dy}{du} = \dfrac{1}{2\sqrt{u}}$

    $\dfrac{du}{dx} = 4x^3 + 10x$

    $\dfrac{dy}{dx} = \dfrac{2x^3 + 5x}{\sqrt{x^4 + 5x^2 + 3}}$

4. $\dfrac{dy}{du} = -\dfrac{5}{u^6}$

    $\dfrac{du}{dx} = \dfrac{1}{3\sqrt[3]{x^2}}$

    $\dfrac{dy}{dx} = -\dfrac{5}{3x^2\sqrt[3]{x^2}}$

5. $\dfrac{dy}{du} = 4e^{4u}$

    $\dfrac{du}{dx} = 3x^2 + 7$

    $\dfrac{dy}{dx} = 4\left(3x^2 + 7\right)e^{4x^3 + 28x}$

6. $\dfrac{dy}{du} = 8\cos 8u$

    $\dfrac{du}{dx} = -12\sin 12x$

    $\dfrac{dy}{dx} = -96\sin 12x\cos\left(8\cos 12x\right)$

7. $\dfrac{dy}{du} = \dfrac{10u + 9}{5u^2 + 9u}$

    $\dfrac{du}{dx} = 2x + 3$

    $\dfrac{dy}{dx} = \dfrac{20x + 39}{10x + 24}$

8. $\dfrac{dy}{du} = 2u \cdot 3^{u^2}\,\mathrm{Ln}\,3$

    $\dfrac{du}{dx} = 1$

    $\dfrac{dy}{dx} = 2\left(x - 1\right) \cdot 3^{(x-1)^2}\,\mathrm{Ln}\,3$

9. $\dfrac{dy}{du} = \left(2u - 8\right)\sec^2\left(u^2 - 8u\right)$

    $\dfrac{du}{dx} = -\dfrac{1}{x^2}$

    $\dfrac{dy}{dx} = \left(-\dfrac{2}{x^3} + \dfrac{8}{x^2}\right)\sec^2\left(\dfrac{1}{x^2} - \dfrac{8}{x}\right)$

10. $\dfrac{dy}{du} = \dfrac{3}{u\,\mathrm{Ln}\,2}$

    $\dfrac{du}{dx} = -\dfrac{1}{x\sqrt{x}}$

    $\dfrac{dy}{dx} = -\dfrac{3}{2x\,\mathrm{Ln}\,2}$

Solutions

1. $y = u^3; \qquad u = 2x + 1$

    $\dfrac{dy}{du} = 3u^2$

    $\dfrac{du}{dx} = 2$

    $\dfrac{dy}{dx} = \dfrac{dy}{du} \cdot \dfrac{du}{dx}$

    $\Rightarrow \quad \dfrac{dy}{dx} = 3u^2 \cdot 2$

    $\dfrac{dy}{dx} = 6u^2$

2. $y = u^2 + 3u; \quad u = x^2 - 3$

    $\dfrac{dy}{du} = 2u + 3$

    $\dfrac{du}{dx} = 2x$

    $\dfrac{dy}{dx} = \dfrac{dy}{du} \cdot \dfrac{du}{dx}$

    $\Rightarrow \quad \dfrac{dy}{dx} = (2u + 3)(2x)$

    Substituting $u = x^2 - 3$ into $\dfrac{dy}{dx}$, we get:

    $\dfrac{dy}{dx} = \left[2(x^2 - 3) + 3 \right](2x)$

    $\dfrac{dy}{dx} = (2x - 6 + 3)(2x)$

    $\dfrac{dy}{dx} = (2x - 3)(2x)$

    $\dfrac{dy}{dx} = 4x^2 - 6x$

3. $y = \sqrt{u}$; $u = x^4 + 5x^2 + 3$

$y = \sqrt{u} = u^{\frac{1}{2}}$

$\dfrac{dy}{du} = \dfrac{1}{2} u^{-\frac{1}{2}} = \dfrac{1}{2u^{\frac{1}{2}}} = \dfrac{1}{2\sqrt{u}}$

$\dfrac{du}{dx} = 4x^3 + 10x$

$\dfrac{dy}{dx} = \dfrac{dy}{du} \cdot \dfrac{du}{dx}$

$\Rightarrow \quad \dfrac{dy}{dx} = \dfrac{1}{2\sqrt{u}}\left(4x^3 + 10x\right)$

Substituting $u = x^4 + 5x^2 + 3$ into $\dfrac{dy}{dx}$:

$\dfrac{dy}{dx} = \dfrac{1}{2\sqrt{x^4 + 5x^2 + 3}}\left(4x^3 + 10x\right)$

$\dfrac{dy}{dx} = \dfrac{4x^3 + 10x}{2\sqrt{x^4 + 5x^2 + 3}}$

$\dfrac{dy}{dx} = \dfrac{2x^3 + 5x}{\sqrt{x^4 + 5x^2 + 3}}$

4. $y = \dfrac{1}{u^5}$; $u = \sqrt[3]{x}$

$y = \dfrac{1}{u^5} = u^{-5}$ $u = \sqrt[3]{x} = x^{\frac{1}{3}}$

$\dfrac{dy}{du} = -5u^{-6} = -\dfrac{5}{u^6}$

$\dfrac{du}{dx} = \dfrac{1}{3} x^{-\frac{2}{3}} = \dfrac{1}{3\sqrt[3]{x^2}}$

$\dfrac{dy}{dx} = \dfrac{dy}{du} \cdot \dfrac{du}{dx}$

$\Rightarrow \quad \dfrac{dy}{dx} = -\dfrac{5}{u^6}\left(\dfrac{1}{3\sqrt[3]{x^2}}\right)$

calculation cont. on next page...

Solution #4 from previous page...

Substituting $u = \sqrt[3]{x}$ into $\dfrac{dy}{dx}$:

$$\frac{dy}{dx} = -\frac{5}{\left(\sqrt[3]{x}\right)^6}\left(\frac{1}{3\sqrt[3]{x^2}}\right)$$

$$\frac{dy}{dx} = -\frac{5}{x^2}\left(\frac{1}{3\sqrt[3]{x^2}}\right)$$

$$\frac{dy}{dx} = -\frac{5}{3x^2\sqrt[3]{x^2}}$$

5. $y = e^{4u}$; $\qquad u = x^3 + 7x$

$$\frac{dy}{du} = 4e^{4u}$$

$$\frac{du}{dx} = 3x^2 + 7$$

$$\frac{dy}{dx} = \frac{dy}{du} \cdot \frac{du}{dx}$$

$\Rightarrow \quad \dfrac{dy}{dx} = 4e^{4u}\left(3x^2 + 7\right)$

Substituting $u = x^3 + 7x$ into $\dfrac{dy}{dx}$:

$$\frac{dy}{dx} = 4e^{4\left(x^3+7x\right)}\left(3x^2 + 7\right)$$

$$\frac{dy}{dx} = 4\left(3x^2 + 7\right)e^{4x^3+28x}$$

6. $y = \sin 8u$; $\qquad u = \cos 12x$

$$\frac{dy}{du} = 8\cos 8u$$

$$\frac{du}{dx} = -12\sin 12x$$

$$\frac{dy}{dx} = \frac{dy}{du} \cdot \frac{du}{dx}$$

$\Rightarrow \quad \dfrac{dy}{dx} = 8\cos 8u\left(-12\sin 12x\right)$

calculation cont. on next page...

Solution #6 from previous page...

Substituting $u = \cos 12x$ into $\dfrac{dy}{dx}$:

$$\frac{dy}{dx} = 8\cos 8\left(\cos 12x\right)\left(-12\sin 12x\right)$$

$$\frac{dy}{dx} = -96\sin 12x \cos\left(8\cos 12x\right)$$

7. $y = \operatorname{Ln}\left(5u^2 + 9u\right); \quad u = x^2 + 3x$

$$\frac{dy}{du} = \frac{10u + 9}{5u^2 + 9u}$$

$$\frac{du}{dx} = 2x + 3$$

$$\frac{dy}{dx} = \frac{dy}{du} \cdot \frac{du}{dx}$$

$\Rightarrow \quad \dfrac{dy}{dx} = \dfrac{10u + 9}{5u^2 + 9u}\left(2x + 3\right)$

Since $u = x^2 + 3x$,

$$\frac{dy}{dx} = \frac{10\left(2x + 3\right) + 9}{5\left(2x + 3\right)^2 + 9\left(2x + 3\right)}\left(2x + 3\right)$$

$$\frac{dy}{dx} = \frac{10\left(2x + 3\right) + 9}{5\left(2x + 3\right) + 9}$$

$$\frac{dy}{dx} = \frac{20x + 30 + 9}{10x + 15 + 9}$$

$$\frac{dy}{dx} = \frac{20x + 39}{10x + 24}$$

8. $y = 3^{u^2}; \qquad u = x - 1$

$\dfrac{dy}{du} = 2u \cdot 3^{u^2} \, \text{Ln } 3$

$\dfrac{du}{dx} = 1$

$\dfrac{dy}{dx} = \dfrac{dy}{du} \cdot \dfrac{du}{dx}$

$\Rightarrow \quad \dfrac{dy}{dx} = 2u \cdot 3^{u^2} \, \text{Ln } 3 \cdot 1 = 2u \; 3^{u^2} \, \text{Ln } 3$

Substituting $u = x - 1$ into $\dfrac{dy}{dx}$:

$\dfrac{dy}{dx} = 2(x - 1) \cdot 3^{(x-1)^2} \, \text{Ln } 3$

9. $y = \tan\left(u^2 - 8u\right); \qquad u = \dfrac{1}{x}$

$\dfrac{dy}{du} = (2u - 8)\sec^2\left(u^2 - 8u\right)$

$\dfrac{du}{dx} = -\dfrac{1}{x^2}$

$\dfrac{dy}{dx} = \dfrac{dy}{du} \cdot \dfrac{du}{dx}$

$\Rightarrow \quad \dfrac{dy}{dx} = (2u - 8)\sec^2\left(u^2 - 8u\right) \cdot \left(-\dfrac{1}{x^2}\right)$

Substituting $u = \dfrac{1}{x}$ into $\dfrac{dy}{dx}$ we have:

$\dfrac{dy}{dx} = \left[2\left(\dfrac{1}{x}\right) - 8\right]\sec^2\left[\left(\dfrac{1}{x}\right)^2 - 8\left(\dfrac{1}{x}\right)\right] \cdot \left(-\dfrac{1}{x^2}\right)$

$\dfrac{dy}{dx} = \left(\dfrac{2}{x} - 8\right)\left(-\dfrac{1}{x^2}\right)\sec^2\left(\dfrac{1}{x^2} - \dfrac{8}{x}\right)$

$\dfrac{dy}{dx} = \left(-\dfrac{2}{x^3} + \dfrac{8}{x^2}\right)\sec^2\left(\dfrac{1}{x^2} - \dfrac{8}{x}\right)$

10. $y = \log_2 u^3;$ $u = \dfrac{2}{\sqrt{x}}$

$$u = \frac{2}{\sqrt{x}} = \frac{2}{x^{\frac{1}{2}}} = 2x^{-\frac{1}{2}}$$

$$\frac{dy}{du} = \frac{1}{u^3 \, \text{Ln} \, 2} \cdot 3u^2$$

$$\frac{dy}{du} = \frac{3}{u \, \text{Ln} \, 2}$$

$$\frac{du}{dx} = -\frac{1}{2}\left(2x^{-\frac{3}{2}}\right)$$

$$\frac{du}{dx} = -x^{-\frac{3}{2}}$$

$$\frac{du}{dx} = -\frac{1}{x^{\frac{3}{2}}}$$

$$\frac{du}{dx} = -\frac{1}{x\sqrt{x}}$$

$$\frac{dy}{dx} = \frac{dy}{du} \cdot \frac{du}{dx}$$

$$\Rightarrow \quad \frac{dy}{dx} = \frac{3}{u \, \text{Ln} \, 2}\left(-\frac{1}{x\sqrt{x}}\right)$$

Substituting $u = \dfrac{2}{\sqrt{x}}$ into $\dfrac{dy}{dx}$:

$$\frac{dy}{dx} = \frac{3}{\dfrac{2}{\sqrt{x}} \, \text{Ln} \, 2}\left(-\frac{1}{x\sqrt{x}}\right)$$

$$\frac{dy}{dx} = -\frac{3}{2x \, \text{Ln} \, 2}$$

DERIVATIVES
AND SLOPE

15

For each of the following functions, find the slope of the tangent line at the given point.

1. $f(x) = x^2$ at $x = 1$

2. $f(x) = x^3$ at $x = -1$

3. $f(x) = 2x - 3x^2$ at $x = 2$

4. $f(x) = \sqrt{x}$ at $x = 4$

5. $f(x) = -x^2$ at $x = 0$

6. $f(x) = 8$ at $x = 5$

7. $f(x) = e^{3x}$ at $x = 0$

8. $f(x) = \text{Ln } x$ at $x = 2$

9. $f(x) = \sin x$ at $x = \pi$

10. $f(x) = \tan x$ at $x = \dfrac{\pi}{4}$

Notes

1. 2

2. 3

3. -10

4. $\dfrac{1}{4}$

5. 0

6. 0

7. 3

8. $\dfrac{1}{2}$

9. -1

10. $\sqrt{2}$

Solutions

For each of the following, our strategy will be to find the derivative of the given function and then evaluate the derivative at the given point.

1. $f(x) = x^2$ at $x = 1$

    $f'(x) = 2x$

    $f'(1) = 2(1) = 2$

    The slope of the tangent line to the function $f(x) = x^2$ at $x = 1$ is 2.

2. $f(x) = x^3$ at $x = -1$

    $f'(x) = 3x^2$

    $f'(-1) = 3(-1)^2 = 3$

    The slope of the tangent line to the function $f(x) = x^3$ at $x = -1$ is 3.

3. $f(x) = 2x - 3x^2$ at $x = 2$

    $f'(x) = 2 - 6x$

    $f'(2) = 2 - 6(2) = 2 - 12 = -10$

    The slope of the tangent line to the function $f(x) = 2x - 3x^2$ at $x = 2$ is -10.

4. $f(x) = \sqrt{x}$ at $x = 4$

    $f(x) = x^{\frac{1}{2}}$

    $f'(x) = \frac{1}{2} x^{-\frac{1}{2}} = \frac{1}{2\sqrt{x}}$

    Focusing on the principal root:

    $f'(4) = \frac{1}{2\sqrt{4}} = \frac{1}{2(2)} = \frac{1}{4}$

    The slope of the tangent line to the function $f(x) = \sqrt{x}$ at $x = 4$ is $\frac{1}{4}$.

5. $f(x) = -x^2$ at $x = 0$

$f'(x) = -2x$

$f'(0) = -2(0) = 0$

The slope of the tangent line to the function $f(x) = -x^2$ at $x = 0$ is 0.

6. $f(x) = 8$ at $x = 5$

$f'(x) = 0$

The fact that the derivative is identically zero means that the function is a horizontal straight line. Consequently, the slope of the tangent line at all points is identically zero.

$$f'(5) = 0$$

7. $f(x) = e^{3x}$ at $x = 0$

$f'(x) = 3e^{3x}$

$f'(0) = 3e^{3(0)}$

$f'(0) = 3e^0$

$f'(0) = 3(1)$

$f'(0) = 3$

The slope of the tangent line to the function $f(x) = e^{3x}$ at $x = 0$ is 3.

8. $f(x) = \text{Ln } x$ at $x = 2$

$f'(x) = \dfrac{1}{x}$

$f'(2) = \dfrac{1}{2}$

The slope of the tangent line to the function $f(x) = \text{Ln } x$ at $x = 2$ is $\dfrac{1}{2}$.

9. $f(x) = \sin x$ at $x = \pi$

$f'(x) = \cos x$

$f'(\pi) = \cos \pi = -1$

The slope of the tangent line to the function $f(x) = \sin x$ at $x = \pi$ is -1.

10. $f(x) = \tan x$ at $x = \dfrac{\pi}{4}$

$f'(x) = \sec x \tan x$

$f'\left(\dfrac{\pi}{4}\right) = \sec \dfrac{\pi}{4} \tan \dfrac{\pi}{4}$

$f'\left(\dfrac{\pi}{4}\right) = \dfrac{2}{\sqrt{2}} \, (1)$

$f'\left(\dfrac{\pi}{4}\right) = \dfrac{2}{\sqrt{2}}$

Or, rationalizing the denominator:

$f'\left(\dfrac{\pi}{4}\right) = \dfrac{2}{\sqrt{2}} \cdot \dfrac{\sqrt{2}}{\sqrt{2}} = \dfrac{2\sqrt{2}}{2} = \sqrt{2}$

The slope of the tangent line to the function $f(x) = \tan x$ at $x = \dfrac{\pi}{4}$ is $\sqrt{2}$.

HIGHER ORDER DERIVATIVES

16

Find the first, second, and third derivatives of each of the following functions.

Notes

1. $f(x) = x^5$

2. $f(x) = 3x^4 - x^2$

3. $f(x) = 5x^2 + 8x$

4. $f(x) = \sqrt{x}$

5. $f(x) = e^{2x}$

6. $f(x) = \sin x$

7. $f(x) = \cos 2x$

8. $f(x) = e^x$

9. $f(x) = \dfrac{1}{x^6}$

10. $f(x) = (2x + 5)^3$

Solutions

1. $f(x) = x^5$

    $f'(x) = 5x^4$

    $f''(x) = 20x^3$

    $f'''(x) = 60x^2$

2. $f(x) = 3x^4 - x^2$

    $f'(x) = 12x^3 - 2x$

    $f''(x) = 36x^2 - 2$

    $f'''(x) = 72x$

3. $f(x) = 5x^2 + 8x$

    $f'(x) = 10x + 8$

    $f''(x) = 10$

    $f'''(x) = 0$

4. $f(x) = \sqrt{x}$

    $f(x) = x^{\frac{1}{2}}$

    $f'(x) = \frac{1}{2}x^{-\frac{1}{2}} = \frac{1}{2x^{\frac{1}{2}}} = \frac{1}{2\sqrt{x}} = \frac{\sqrt{x}}{2x}$

    $f''(x) = -\frac{1}{4}x^{-\frac{3}{2}} = -\frac{1}{4x^{\frac{3}{2}}} = -\frac{1}{4x\sqrt{x}} = -\frac{\sqrt{x}}{4x^2}$

    $f'''(x) = \frac{3}{8}x^{-\frac{5}{2}} = \frac{3}{8x^{\frac{5}{2}}} = \frac{3}{8x^2\sqrt{x}} = \frac{3\sqrt{x}}{8x^3}$

5. $f(x) = e^{2x}$

    $f'(x) = 2e^{2x}$

    $f''(x) = 4e^{2x}$

    $f'''(x) = 8e^{2x}$

6. $f(x) = \sin x$

   $f'(x) = \cos x$

   $f''(x) = -\sin x$

   $f'''(x) = -\cos x$

7. $f(x) = \cos 2x$

   $f'(x) = -2\sin 2x$

   $f''(x) = -4\cos 2x$

   $f'''(x) = 8\sin 2x$

8. $f(x) = e^x$

   $f'(x) = e^x$

   $f''(x) = e^x$

   $f'''(x) = e^x$

9. $f(x) = \dfrac{1}{x^6}$

   $f(x) = x^{-6}$

   $f'(x) = -6x^{-7} = -\dfrac{6}{x^7}$

   $f''(x) = 42x^{-8} = \dfrac{42}{x^8}$

   $f'''(x) = -336x^{-9} = \dfrac{-336}{x^9}$

10. $f(x) = (2x+5)^3$

    $f'(x) = 3(2)(2x+5)^2 = 6(2x+5)^2$

    $f''(x) = 6(2)(2)(2x+5) = 24(2x+5) = 48x+120$

    $f'''(x) = 48$

PARTIAL
DERIVATIVES

For each of the following, find $\dfrac{\partial y}{\partial x}$ and $\dfrac{\partial y}{\partial z}$.

1. $y = 3x + z^2$

2. $y = x^3 - z^4$

3. $y = e^{5x} + \text{Ln } z^2$

4. $y = xz$

5. $y = x^2 z^3$

6. $y = xz^2 - x^2 z$

7. $y = \left(x^2 + 3z\right)^3$

8. $y = \left(6x^3 - z^2\right)\left(z^4 + x\right)$

9. $y = \dfrac{5x + 6z}{x - z}$

10. $y = \sin xz$

For each of the following, find $\dfrac{\partial y}{\partial x}$, $\dfrac{\partial y}{\partial z}$, and $\dfrac{\partial y}{\partial w}$.

11. $y = xzw$

12. $y = x^2 z - z^2 w$

13. $y = 5x + 6zw^2$

14. $y = \sqrt{3x + 2y + 4z}$

15. $y = \cos xzw$

16. $y = e^{xw} - e^{z^2}$

17. $y = \dfrac{1}{\sqrt[3]{zw + xz}}$

18. $y = \dfrac{xwz}{x + w + z}$

19. $y = \dfrac{x}{z^2} + \dfrac{z}{w^2} + \dfrac{w}{x^3}$

20. $y = \sin\left(e^{x^2 w z^3}\right)$

Answer Key

1. $\dfrac{\partial y}{\partial x} = 3$

   $\dfrac{\partial y}{\partial z} = 2z$

2. $\dfrac{\partial y}{\partial x} = 3x^2$

   $\dfrac{\partial y}{\partial z} = -4z^3$

3. $\dfrac{\partial y}{\partial x} = 5e^{5x}$

   $\dfrac{\partial y}{\partial z} = \dfrac{2}{z}$

4. $\dfrac{\partial y}{\partial x} = z$

   $\dfrac{\partial y}{\partial z} = x$

5. $\dfrac{\partial y}{\partial x} = 2xz^3$

   $\dfrac{\partial y}{\partial z} = 3x^2z^2$

6. $\dfrac{\partial y}{\partial x} = z^2 - 2xz$

   $\dfrac{\partial y}{\partial z} = 2xz - x^2$

7. $\dfrac{\partial y}{\partial x} = 6x\left(x^2 + 3z\right)^2$

   $\dfrac{\partial y}{\partial z} = 9\left(x^2 + 3z\right)^2$

8. $\dfrac{\partial y}{\partial x} = 24x^3 - z^2 + 18x^2z^4$

   $\dfrac{\partial y}{\partial z} = 24x^3z^3 - 6z^5 - 2xz$

9. $\dfrac{\partial y}{\partial x} = -\dfrac{11z}{\left(x-z\right)^2}$

   $\dfrac{\partial y}{\partial z} = \dfrac{11x}{\left(x-z\right)^2}$

10. $\dfrac{\partial y}{\partial x} = z \cos xz$

    $\dfrac{\partial y}{\partial z} = x \cos xz$

11. $\dfrac{\partial y}{\partial x} = zw$

    $\dfrac{\partial y}{\partial z} = xw$

    $\dfrac{\partial y}{\partial w} = xz$

12. $\dfrac{\partial y}{\partial x} = 2xz$

    $\dfrac{\partial y}{\partial z} = x^2 - 2zw$

    $\dfrac{\partial y}{\partial w} = -z^2$

13. $\dfrac{\partial y}{\partial x} = 5$

    $\dfrac{\partial y}{\partial z} = 6w^2$

    $\dfrac{\partial y}{\partial w} = 12zw$

14. $\dfrac{\partial y}{\partial x} = \dfrac{3}{2\sqrt{3x + 2w + 4z}}$

    $\dfrac{\partial y}{\partial z} = \dfrac{2}{\sqrt{3x + 2w + 4z}}$

    $\dfrac{\partial y}{\partial w} = \dfrac{1}{\sqrt{3x + 2w + 4z}}$

15. $\dfrac{\partial y}{\partial x} = -zw \sin xzw$

    $\dfrac{\partial y}{\partial z} = -xw \sin xzw$

    $\dfrac{\partial y}{\partial w} = -xz \sin xzw$

16. $\dfrac{\partial y}{\partial x} = we^{xw}$

    $\dfrac{\partial y}{\partial z} = -2ze^{z^2}$

    $\dfrac{\partial y}{\partial w} = xe^{xw}$

17. $\dfrac{\partial y}{\partial x} = -\dfrac{z}{3\left(zw + xz\right)\sqrt[3]{zw + xz}}$

    $\dfrac{\partial y}{\partial z} = -\dfrac{w + x}{3\left(zw + xz\right)\sqrt[3]{zw + xz}}$

    $\dfrac{\partial y}{\partial w} = -\dfrac{z}{3\left(zw + xz\right)\sqrt[3]{zw + xz}}$

18. $\dfrac{\partial y}{\partial x} = \dfrac{w^2z + wz^2}{\left(x + w + z\right)^2}$

    $\dfrac{\partial y}{\partial z} = \dfrac{x^2w + xw^2}{\left(x + w + z\right)^2}$

    $\dfrac{\partial y}{\partial w} = \dfrac{x^2z + xz^2}{\left(x + w + z\right)^2}$

19. $\dfrac{\partial y}{\partial x} = \dfrac{1}{z^2} - \dfrac{3w}{x^4}$

    $\dfrac{\partial y}{\partial z} = -\dfrac{2x}{z^3} + \dfrac{1}{w^2}$

    $\dfrac{\partial y}{\partial w} = -\dfrac{2z}{w^3} + \dfrac{1}{x^3}$

20. $\dfrac{\partial y}{\partial x} = 2xwz^3 e^{x^2 wz^3} \cos\left(e^{x^2 wz^3}\right)$

    $\dfrac{\partial y}{\partial z} = 3x^2wz^2 e^{x^2 wz^3} \cos\left(e^{x^2 wz^3}\right)$

    $\dfrac{\partial y}{\partial w} = x^2z^3 e^{x^2 wz^3} \cos\left(e^{x^2 wz^3}\right)$

Solutions

1. $y = 3x + z^2$

$$\frac{\partial y}{\partial x} = 3$$

$$\frac{\partial y}{\partial z} = 2z$$

2. $y = x^3 - z^4$

$$\frac{\partial y}{\partial x} = 3x^2$$

$$\frac{\partial y}{\partial z} = -4z^3$$

3. $y = e^{5x} + \text{Ln } z^2$

$$\frac{\partial y}{\partial x} = 5e^{5x}$$

$$\frac{\partial y}{\partial z} = \frac{2z}{z^2} = \frac{2}{z}$$

4. $y = xz$

$$\frac{\partial y}{\partial x} = z$$

$$\frac{\partial y}{\partial z} = x$$

5. $y = x^2 z^3$

$$\frac{\partial y}{\partial x} = 2xz^3$$

$$\frac{\partial y}{\partial z} = 3x^2 z^2$$

6. $y = xz^2 - x^2 z$

$$\frac{\partial y}{\partial x} = z^2 - 2xz$$

$$\frac{\partial y}{\partial z} = 2xz - x^2$$

7. $y = \left(x^2 + 3z\right)^3$

Using the Power Rule to find both partial derivatives:

$$\frac{\partial y}{\partial x} = 3\left(x^2 + 3z\right)^2 (2x)$$

$$\frac{\partial y}{\partial x} = 6x\left(x^2 + 3z\right)^2$$

$$\frac{\partial y}{\partial z} = 3\left(x^2 + 3z\right)^2 (3)$$

$$\frac{\partial y}{\partial z} = 9\left(x^2 + 3z\right)^2$$

8. $y = \left(6x^3 - z^2\right)\left(z^4 + x\right)$

Using the Product Rule to find both partial derivatives:

$$\frac{\partial y}{\partial x} = \left(6x^3 - z^2\right)(1) + \left(z^4 + x\right)\left(18x^2\right)$$

$$\frac{\partial y}{\partial x} = 6x^3 - z^2 + 18x^2 z^4 + 18x^3$$

$$\frac{\partial y}{\partial x} = 24x^3 - z^2 + 18x^2 z^4$$

$$\frac{\partial y}{\partial z} = \left(6x^3 - z^2\right)\left(4z^3\right) + \left(z^4 + x\right)(-2z)$$

$$\frac{\partial y}{\partial z} = 24x^3 z^3 - 4z^5 - 2z^5 - 2xz$$

$$\frac{\partial y}{\partial z} = 24x^3 z^3 - 6z^5 - 2xz$$

9. $y = \dfrac{5x + 6z}{x - z}$

Using the Quotient Rule to find both partial derivatives:

$$\frac{\partial y}{\partial x} = \frac{(x-z)(5) - (5x + 6z)(1)}{(x-z)^2}$$

$$\frac{\partial y}{\partial x} = \frac{5x - 5z - 5x - 6z}{(x-z)^2}$$

$$\frac{\partial y}{\partial x} = -\frac{11z}{(x-z)^2}$$

$$\frac{\partial y}{\partial z} = \frac{(x-z)(6) - (5x + 6z)(-1)}{(x-z)^2}$$

$$\frac{\partial y}{\partial z} = \frac{6x - 6z + 5x + 6z}{(x-z)^2}$$

$$\frac{\partial y}{\partial z} = \frac{11x}{(x-z)^2}$$

10. $y = \sin xz$

$$\frac{\partial y}{\partial x} = z \cos xz$$

$$\frac{\partial y}{\partial z} = x \cos xz$$

11. $y = xzw$

$$\frac{\partial y}{\partial x} = zw$$

$$\frac{\partial y}{\partial z} = xw$$

$$\frac{\partial y}{\partial w} = xz$$

12. $y = x^2 z - z^2 w$

$$\frac{\partial y}{\partial x} = 2xz$$

$$\frac{\partial y}{\partial z} = x^2 - 2zw$$

$$\frac{\partial y}{\partial w} = -z^2$$

13. $y = 5x + 6zw^2$

$$\frac{\partial y}{\partial x} = 5$$

$$\frac{\partial y}{\partial z} = 6w^2$$

$$\frac{\partial y}{\partial w} = 12zw$$

14. $y = \sqrt{3x + 2w + 4z}$

$$y = (3x + 2w + 4z)^{\frac{1}{2}}$$

Using the Power Rule, we find each of the required partial derivatives:

$$\frac{\partial y}{\partial x} = \frac{1}{2}(3x + 2w + 4z)^{-\frac{1}{2}}(3)$$

$$\frac{\partial y}{\partial x} = \frac{3}{2(3x + 2w + 4z)^{\frac{1}{2}}}$$

$$\frac{\partial y}{\partial x} = \frac{3}{2\sqrt{3x + 2w + 4z}}$$

$$\frac{\partial y}{\partial z} = \frac{1}{2}(3x + 2w + 4z)^{-\frac{1}{2}}(4)$$

$$\frac{\partial y}{\partial z} = \frac{2}{(3x + 2w + 4z)^{\frac{1}{2}}}$$

$$\frac{\partial y}{\partial z} = \frac{2}{\sqrt{3x + 2w + 4z}}$$

$$\frac{\partial y}{\partial w} = \frac{1}{2}(3x + 2w + 4z)^{-\frac{1}{2}}(2)$$

$$\frac{\partial y}{\partial w} = \frac{1}{(3x + 2w + 4z)^{\frac{1}{2}}}$$

$$\frac{\partial y}{\partial w} = \frac{1}{\sqrt{3x + 2w + 4z}}$$

15. $y = \cos xzw$

$$\frac{\partial y}{\partial x} = -zw \sin xzw$$

$$\frac{\partial y}{\partial z} = -xw \sin xzw$$

$$\frac{\partial y}{\partial w} = -xz \sin xzw$$

16. $y = e^{xw} - e^{z^2}$

$$\frac{\partial y}{\partial x} = we^{xw}$$

$$\frac{\partial y}{\partial z} = -2ze^{z^2}$$

$$\frac{\partial y}{\partial w} = xe^{xw}$$

17. $y = \dfrac{1}{\sqrt[3]{zw + xz}}$

$$y = \frac{1}{(zw + xz)^{\frac{1}{3}}}$$

$$y = (zw + xz)^{-\frac{1}{3}}$$

Using the Power Rule to find each of the partial derivatives:

$$\frac{\partial y}{\partial x} = -\frac{1}{3}(zw + xz)^{-\frac{4}{3}}(z)$$

$$\frac{\partial y}{\partial x} = -\frac{z}{3(zw + xz)^{\frac{4}{3}}}$$

$$\frac{\partial y}{\partial x} = -\frac{z}{3(zw + xz)\sqrt[3]{zw + xz}}$$

$$\frac{\partial y}{\partial w} = -\frac{1}{3}(zw + xz)^{-\frac{4}{3}}(z)$$

$$\frac{\partial y}{\partial w} = -\frac{z}{3(zw + xz)^{\frac{4}{3}}}$$

$$\frac{\partial y}{\partial w} = -\frac{z}{3(zw + xz)\sqrt[3]{zw + xz}}$$

$$\frac{\partial y}{\partial z} = -\frac{1}{3}(zw + xz)^{-\frac{4}{3}}(w + x)$$

$$\frac{\partial y}{\partial z} = -\frac{w + x}{3(zw + xz)^{\frac{4}{3}}}$$

$$\frac{\partial y}{\partial z} = -\frac{w + x}{3(zw + xz)\sqrt[3]{zw + xz}}$$

18. $y = \dfrac{xwz}{x+w+z}$

Using the Quotient Rule, we find the three required partial derivatives:

$$\frac{\partial y}{\partial x} = \frac{(x+w+z)(wz)-(xwz)(1)}{(x+w+z)^2}$$

$$\frac{\partial y}{\partial x} = \frac{xwz+w^2z+wz^2-xwz}{(x+w+z)^2}$$

$$\frac{\partial y}{\partial x} = \frac{w^2z+wz^2}{(x+w+z)^2}$$

$$\frac{\partial y}{\partial z} = \frac{(x+w+z)(xw)-(xwz)(1)}{(x+w+z)^2}$$

$$\frac{\partial y}{\partial z} = \frac{x^2w+xw^2+zxw-xwz}{(x+w+z)^2}$$

$$\frac{\partial y}{\partial z} = \frac{x^2w+xw^2}{(x+w+z)^2}$$

$$\frac{\partial y}{\partial w} = \frac{(x+w+z)(xz)-(xwz)(1)}{(x+w+z)^2}$$

$$\frac{\partial y}{\partial w} = \frac{x^2z+wxz+xz^2-xwz}{(x+w+z)^2}$$

$$\frac{\partial y}{\partial w} = \frac{x^2z+xz^2}{(x+w+z)^2}$$

19. $y = \dfrac{x}{z^2} + \dfrac{z}{w^2} + \dfrac{w}{x^3}$

To find $\dfrac{\partial y}{\partial x}$, we begin by rewriting the equation as:

$$y = \frac{1}{z^2} \cdot x + \frac{z}{w^2} + wx^{-3}$$

Finding the partial derivative, we have:

$$\frac{\partial y}{\partial x} = \frac{1}{z^2} - 3wx^{-4}$$

$$\frac{\partial y}{\partial x} = \frac{1}{z^2} - \frac{3w}{x^4}$$

Solution #19 cont. on next page...

Solution #19 from previous page...

To find $\dfrac{\partial y}{\partial z}$, we begin by rewriting the equation as:

$$y = xz^{-2} + \frac{1}{w^2} \cdot z + \frac{w}{x^3}$$

Finding the partial derivative, we have:

$$\frac{\partial y}{\partial z} = -2xz^{-3} + \frac{1}{w^2}$$

$$\frac{\partial y}{\partial z} = -\frac{2x}{z^3} + \frac{1}{w^2}$$

Finally, to find $\dfrac{\partial y}{\partial w}$, we begin by rewriting the equation as:

$$y = \frac{x}{z^2} + zw^{-2} + \frac{1}{x^3} \cdot w$$

$$\Rightarrow \quad \frac{\partial y}{\partial w} = -2zw^{-3} + \frac{1}{x^3}$$

$$\frac{\partial y}{\partial w} = -\frac{2z}{w^3} + \frac{1}{x^3}$$

20. $y = \sin\left(e^{x^2 w z^3}\right)$

$$\frac{\partial y}{\partial x} = 2xwz^3 e^{x^2 w z^3} \cos\left(e^{x^2 w z^3}\right)$$

$$\frac{\partial y}{\partial z} = 3x^2 wz^2 e^{x^2 w z^3} \cos\left(e^{x^2 w z^3}\right)$$

$$\frac{\partial y}{\partial w} = x^2 z^3 e^{x^2 w z^3} \cos\left(e^{x^2 w z^3}\right)$$

HIGHER ORDER
PARTIAL DERIVATIVES

For each of the following, find $\dfrac{\partial^2 y}{\partial x^2}$, $\dfrac{\partial^3 y}{\partial x^3}$, $\dfrac{\partial^2 y}{\partial z^2}$, and $\dfrac{\partial^3 y}{\partial z^3}$.

1. $y = x^4 + z^5$

2. $y = x^3 z^6$

3. $y = e^{xz}$

4. $y = \sin xz$

5. $y = \cos(x + 2z)$

6. $y = \sqrt{x + 3z}$

7. $y = \dfrac{x^5}{z}$

8. $y = (x + z)(x^2 - 3z)$

9. $y = \dfrac{1}{xz}$

10. $y = \text{Ln}\left(\dfrac{x^2 + z}{x - z^2}\right)$

Notes

Answer Key

1. $\dfrac{\partial^2 y}{\partial x^2} = 12x^2$ $\dfrac{\partial^2 y}{\partial z^2} = 20z^3$

$\dfrac{\partial^3 y}{\partial x^3} = 24x$ $\dfrac{\partial^3 y}{\partial z^3} = 60z^2$

2. $\dfrac{\partial^2 y}{\partial x^2} = 6xz^6$ $\dfrac{\partial^2 y}{\partial z^2} = 30x^3 z^4$

$\dfrac{\partial^3 y}{\partial x^3} = 6z^6$ $\dfrac{\partial^3 y}{\partial z^3} = 120x^3 z^3$

3. $\dfrac{\partial^2 y}{\partial x^2} = z^2 e^{xz}$ $\dfrac{\partial^2 y}{\partial z^2} = x^2 e^{xz}$

$\dfrac{\partial^3 y}{\partial x^3} = z^3 e^{xz}$ $\dfrac{\partial^3 y}{\partial z^3} = x^3 e^{xz}$

4. $\dfrac{\partial^2 y}{\partial x^2} = -z^2 \sin xz$ $\dfrac{\partial^2 y}{\partial z^2} = -x^2 \sin xz$

$\dfrac{\partial^3 y}{\partial x^3} = -z^3 \cos xz$ $\dfrac{\partial^3 y}{\partial z^3} = -x^3 \cos xz$

5. $\dfrac{\partial^2 y}{\partial x^2} = -\cos(x+2z)$

$\dfrac{\partial^3 y}{\partial x^3} = \sin(x+2z)$

$\dfrac{\partial^2 y}{\partial z^2} = -4\cos(x+2z)$

$\dfrac{\partial^3 y}{\partial z^3} = 8\sin(x+2z)$

6. $\dfrac{\partial^2 y}{\partial x^2} = -\dfrac{1}{4(x+3z)\sqrt{x+3z}}$

$\dfrac{\partial^3 y}{\partial x^3} = \dfrac{3}{8(x+3z)^2 \sqrt{x+3z}}$

$\dfrac{\partial^2 y}{\partial z^2} = -\dfrac{9}{4(x+3z)\sqrt{x+3z}}$

$\dfrac{\partial^3 y}{\partial z^3} = \dfrac{81}{8(x+3z)^2 \sqrt{x+3z}}$

7. $\dfrac{\partial^2 y}{\partial x^2} = \dfrac{20x^3}{z}$ $\dfrac{\partial^2 y}{\partial z^2} = \dfrac{2x^5}{z^3}$

$\dfrac{\partial^3 y}{\partial x^3} = \dfrac{60x^2}{z}$ $\dfrac{\partial^3 y}{\partial z^3} = -\dfrac{6x^5}{z^4}$

8. $\dfrac{\partial^2 y}{\partial x^2} = 6x+2z$ $\dfrac{\partial^2 y}{\partial z^2} = -6$

$\dfrac{\partial^3 y}{\partial x^3} = 6$ $\dfrac{\partial^3 y}{\partial z^3} = 0$

9. $\dfrac{\partial^2 y}{\partial x^2} = \dfrac{2}{zx^3}$ $\dfrac{\partial^2 y}{\partial z^2} = \dfrac{2}{xz^3}$

$\dfrac{\partial^3 y}{\partial x^3} = -\dfrac{6}{zx^4}$ $\dfrac{\partial^3 y}{\partial z^3} = -\dfrac{6}{xz^4}$

10. $\dfrac{\partial^2 y}{\partial x^2} = \dfrac{-2x^2+2z}{x^4+2x^2z+z^2} + \dfrac{1}{x^2-2xz^2+z^4}$

$\dfrac{\partial^3 y}{\partial x^3} = \dfrac{4x^5-8x^3z-12xz^2}{\left(x^4+2x^2z+z^2\right)^2} - \dfrac{2x-2z^2}{\left(x^2-2xz^2+z^4\right)^2}$

$\dfrac{\partial^2 y}{\partial z^2} = \dfrac{-1}{x^4+2x^2z+z^2} - \dfrac{2x+2z^2}{x^2-2xz^2+z^4}$

$\dfrac{\partial^3 y}{\partial z^3} = \dfrac{2x^2+2z}{\left(x^4+2x^2z+z^2\right)^2} - \dfrac{12x^2z-8xz^3-4z^5}{\left(x^2-2xz^2+z^4\right)^2}$

Solutions

1. $y = x^4 + z^5$

$$\frac{\partial y}{\partial x} = 4x^3 \qquad\qquad \frac{\partial y}{\partial z} = 5z^4$$

$$\frac{\partial^2 y}{\partial x^2} = 12x^2 \qquad\qquad \frac{\partial^2 y}{\partial z^2} = 20z^3$$

$$\frac{\partial^3 y}{\partial x^3} = 24x \qquad\qquad \frac{\partial^3 y}{\partial z^3} = 60z^2$$

2. $y = x^3 z^6$

$$\frac{\partial y}{\partial x} = 3x^2 z^6 \qquad\qquad \frac{\partial y}{\partial z} = 6x^3 z^5$$

$$\frac{\partial^2 y}{\partial x^2} = 6xz^6 \qquad\qquad \frac{\partial^2 y}{\partial z^2} = 30x^3 z^4$$

$$\frac{\partial^3 y}{\partial x^3} = 6z^6 \qquad\qquad \frac{\partial^3 y}{\partial z^3} = 120x^3 z^3$$

3. $y = e^{xz}$

$$\frac{\partial y}{\partial x} = ze^{xz} \qquad\qquad \frac{\partial y}{\partial z} = xe^{xz}$$

$$\frac{\partial^2 y}{\partial x^2} = z^2 e^{xz} \qquad\qquad \frac{\partial^2 y}{\partial z^2} = x^2 e^{xz}$$

$$\frac{\partial^3 y}{\partial x^3} = z^3 e^{xz} \qquad\qquad \frac{\partial^3 y}{\partial z^3} = x^3 e^{xz}$$

4. $y = \sin xz$

$$\frac{\partial y}{\partial x} = z \cos xz \qquad\qquad \frac{\partial y}{\partial z} = x \cos xz$$

$$\frac{\partial^2 y}{\partial x^2} = -z^2 \sin xz \qquad\qquad \frac{\partial^2 y}{\partial z^2} = -x^2 \sin xz$$

$$\frac{\partial^3 y}{\partial x^3} = -z^3 \cos xz \qquad\qquad \frac{\partial^3 y}{\partial z^3} = -x^3 \cos xz$$

5. $y = \cos(x + 2z)$

$$\frac{\partial y}{\partial x} = -\sin(x + 2z) \qquad\qquad \frac{\partial y}{\partial z} = -2\sin(x + 2z)$$

$$\frac{\partial^2 y}{\partial x^2} = -\cos(x + 2z) \qquad\qquad \frac{\partial^2 y}{\partial z^2} = -4\cos(x + 2z)$$

$$\frac{\partial^3 y}{\partial x^3} = \sin(x + 2z) \qquad\qquad \frac{\partial^3 y}{\partial z^3} = 8\sin(x + 2z)$$

6. $y = \sqrt{x + 3z}$

$$y = (x + 3z)^{\frac{1}{2}}$$

Using the Power Rule, we find all of the required partial derivatives.

$$\frac{\partial y}{\partial x} = \underbrace{\frac{1}{2}(x + 3z)^{-\frac{1}{2}}}_{\substack{\text{use this form to calculate} \\ \text{the next partial derivative}}} = \frac{1}{2(x + 3z)^{\frac{1}{2}}} = \frac{1}{2\sqrt{x + 3z}}$$

$$\frac{\partial^2 y}{\partial x^2} = \underbrace{-\frac{1}{4}(x + 3z)^{-\frac{3}{2}}}_{\substack{\text{use this form to calculate} \\ \text{the next partial derivative}}} = -\frac{1}{4(x + 3z)^{\frac{3}{2}}} = -\frac{1}{4(x + 3z)\sqrt{x + 3z}}$$

$$\frac{\partial^3 y}{\partial x^3} = \frac{3}{8}(x + 3z)^{-\frac{5}{2}} = \frac{3}{8(x + 3z)^{\frac{5}{2}}} = \frac{3}{8(x + 3z)^2\sqrt{x + 3z}}$$

$$\frac{\partial y}{\partial z} = \frac{1}{2}(x + 3z)^{-\frac{1}{2}}(3) = \underbrace{\frac{3}{2}(x + 3z)^{-\frac{1}{2}}}_{\substack{\text{use this form to calculate} \\ \text{the next partial derivative}}} = \frac{3}{2(x + 3z)^{\frac{1}{2}}} = \frac{3}{2\sqrt{x + 3z}}$$

$$\frac{\partial^2 y}{\partial z^2} = -\frac{3}{4}(x + 3z)^{-\frac{3}{2}}(3) = \underbrace{-\frac{9}{4}(x + 3z)^{-\frac{3}{2}}}_{\substack{\text{use this form to calculate} \\ \text{the next partial derivative}}} = -\frac{9}{4(x + 3z)^{\frac{3}{2}}} = -\frac{9}{4(x + 3z)\sqrt{x + 3z}}$$

$$\frac{\partial^3 y}{\partial z^3} = \frac{27}{8}(x + 3z)^{-\frac{5}{2}}(3) = \frac{81}{8}(x + 3z)^{-\frac{5}{2}} = \frac{81}{8(x + 3z)^{\frac{5}{2}}} = \frac{81}{8(x + 3z)^2\sqrt{x + 3z}}$$

7. $y = \dfrac{x^5}{z}$

To find the partial derivatives with respect to x, we begin by rewriting the equation as:

$$y = \frac{1}{z} \cdot x^5$$

Thus,

$$\frac{\partial y}{\partial x} = 5\left(\frac{1}{z}\right) \cdot x^4 = \underbrace{\frac{5}{z} x^4}_{} = \frac{5x^4}{z}$$

⌐use this form to calculate
the next partial derivative

$$\frac{\partial^2 y}{\partial x^2} = \underbrace{\frac{20}{z} \cdot x^3}_{} = \frac{20x^3}{z}$$

⌐use this form to calculate
the next partial derivative

$$\frac{\partial^3 y}{\partial x^3} = \frac{60}{z} \cdot x^2 = \frac{60x^2}{z}$$

To find the partial derivatives with respect to z, we begin by rewriting the equation as:

$$y = x^5 z^{-1}$$

Thus,

$$\frac{\partial y}{\partial z} = \underbrace{-x^5 z^{-2}}_{} = -\frac{x^5}{z^2}$$

⌐use this form to calculate
the next partial derivative

$$\frac{\partial^2 y}{\partial z^2} = -(-2)x^5 z^{-3} = \underbrace{2x^5 z^{-3}}_{} = \frac{2x^5}{z^3}$$

⌐use this form to calculate
the next partial derivative

$$\frac{\partial^3 y}{\partial z^3} = 2(-3)x^5 z^{-4} = -\frac{6x^5}{z^4}$$

8. $y = (x+z)(x^2 - 3z)$

Using the Product Rule to find the first partial derivative, we are able to find the required higher order partial derivatives.

$$\frac{\partial y}{\partial x} = (x+z)(2x) + (x^2 - 3z)(1)$$

$$\frac{\partial y}{\partial x} = 2x^2 + 2xz + x^2 - 3z$$

$$\frac{\partial y}{\partial x} = 3x^2 + 2xz - 3z$$

$$\frac{\partial^2 y}{\partial x^2} = 6x + 2z$$

$$\frac{\partial^3 y}{\partial x^3} = 6$$

$$\frac{\partial y}{\partial z} = (x+z)(-3) + (x^2 - 3z)(1)$$

$$\frac{\partial y}{\partial z} = -3x - 3z + x^2 - 3z$$

$$\frac{\partial y}{\partial z} = -3x - 6z + x^2$$

$$\frac{\partial^2 y}{\partial z^2} = -6$$

$$\frac{\partial^3 y}{\partial z^3} = 0$$

9. $y = \dfrac{1}{xz}$

To find the partial derivatives with respect to x, we begin by rewriting the equation as:

$$y = \frac{1}{z} \cdot x^{-1}$$

$\Rightarrow \qquad \dfrac{\partial y}{\partial x} = -1 \left(\dfrac{1}{z} \right) \cdot x^{-2} = \underbrace{-\dfrac{1}{z} \cdot x^{-2}}_{\substack{\text{use this form to calculate} \\ \text{the next partial derivative}}} = -\dfrac{1}{zx^2}$

$\dfrac{\partial^2 y}{\partial x^2} = -(-2) \cdot \dfrac{1}{z} \cdot x^{-3} = \underbrace{\dfrac{2}{z} \cdot x^{-3}}_{\substack{\text{use this form to calculate} \\ \text{the next partial derivative}}} = \dfrac{2}{zx^3}$

$\dfrac{\partial^3 y}{\partial x^3} = -3 \left(\dfrac{2}{z} \right) \cdot x^{-4} = \dfrac{-6}{z} \cdot x^{-4} = -\dfrac{6}{zx^4}$

To find the partial derivatives with respect to z, we begin by rewriting the equation as:

$$y = \frac{1}{x} \cdot z^{-1}$$

$\Rightarrow \qquad \dfrac{\partial y}{\partial z} = -1 \left(\dfrac{1}{x} \right) \cdot z^{-2} = \underbrace{-\dfrac{1}{x} \cdot z^{-2}}_{\substack{\text{use this form to calculate} \\ \text{the next partial derivative}}} = -\dfrac{1}{xz^2}$

$\dfrac{\partial^2 y}{\partial z^2} = -(-2) \cdot \dfrac{1}{x} \cdot z^{-3} = \underbrace{\dfrac{2}{x} \cdot z^{-3}}_{\substack{\text{use this form to calculate} \\ \text{the next partial derivative}}} = \dfrac{2}{xz^3}$

$\dfrac{\partial^3 y}{\partial z^3} = -3 \left(\dfrac{2}{x} \right) \cdot z^{-4} = -\dfrac{6}{xz^4}$

10. $y = \text{Ln}\left(\dfrac{x^2 + z}{x - z^2}\right)$

We begin by drawing on a property of logarithms to rewrite the equation as:

$$y = \text{Ln}\left(x^2 + z\right) - \text{Ln}\left(x - z^2\right)$$

$$\Rightarrow \qquad \frac{\partial y}{\partial x} = \frac{2x}{x^2 + z} - \frac{1}{x - z^2}$$

Using the Quotient Rule to find the derivative of each of the terms:

$$\frac{\partial^2 y}{\partial x^2} = \frac{\left(x^2 + z\right)(2) - 2x(2x)}{\left(x^2 + z\right)^2} - \frac{\left(x - z^2\right)(0) - 1(1)}{\left(x - z^2\right)^2}$$

$$\frac{\partial^2 y}{\partial x^2} = \frac{2x^2 + 2z - 4x^2}{x^4 + 2x^2 z + z^2} - \frac{-1}{x^2 - 2xz^2 + z^4}$$

$$\frac{\partial^2 y}{\partial x^2} = \frac{-2x^2 + 2z}{x^4 + 2x^2 z + z^2} + \frac{1}{x^2 - 2xz^2 + z^4}$$

To find $\dfrac{\partial^3 y}{\partial x^3}$, we first rewrite the 2nd term in $\dfrac{\partial^2 y}{\partial x^2}$:

$$\frac{\partial^2 y}{\partial x^2} = \frac{-2x^2 + 2z}{x^4 + 2x^2 z + z^2} + \left(x^2 - 2xz^2 + z^4\right)^{-1}$$

Using the Quotient Rule on the first term and the Power Rule on the second term we find $\dfrac{\partial^3 y}{\partial x^3}$.

$$\frac{\partial^3 y}{\partial x^3} = \frac{\left(x^4 + 2x^2 z + z^2\right)(-4x) - \left(-2x^2 + 2z\right)\left(4x^3 + 4xz\right)}{\left(x^4 + 2x^2 z + z^2\right)^2} - \left(x^2 - 2xz^2 + z^4\right)^{-2}\left(2x - 2z^2\right)$$

$$\frac{\partial^3 y}{\partial x^3} = \frac{-4x^5 - 8x^3 z - 4xz^2 + 8x^5 + 8x^3 z - 8x^3 z - 8xz^2}{\left(x^4 + 2x^2 z + z^2\right)^2} - \frac{2x - 2z^2}{\left(x^2 - 2xz^2 + z^4\right)^2}$$

$$\frac{\partial^3 y}{\partial x^3} = \frac{4x^5 - 8x^3 z - 12xz^2}{\left(x^4 + 2x^2 z + z^2\right)^2} - \frac{2x - 2z^2}{\left(x^2 - 2xz^2 + z^4\right)^2}$$

Again starting with the rewritten equation:

$$y = \text{Ln}\left(x^2 + z\right) - \text{Ln}\left(x - z^2\right)$$

$$\Rightarrow \quad \frac{\partial y}{\partial z} = \frac{1}{x^2 + z} - \frac{2z}{x - z^2}$$

Using the Quotient Rule on both terms:

$$\frac{\partial^2 y}{\partial z^2} = \frac{\left(x^2 + z\right)(0) - 1(1)}{\left(x^2 + z\right)^2} - \frac{\left(x - z^2\right)(2) - (2z)(-2z)}{\left(x - z^2\right)^2}$$

$$\frac{\partial^2 y}{\partial z^2} = \frac{-1}{x^4 + 2x^2 z + z^2} - \frac{2x - 2z^2 + 4z^2}{x^2 - 2xz^2 + z^4}$$

$$\frac{\partial^2 y}{\partial z^2} = \frac{-1}{x^4 + 2x^2 z + z^2} - \frac{2x + 2z^2}{x^2 - 2xz^2 + z^4}$$

Again using the Quotient Rule on both terms we find $\dfrac{\partial^3 y}{\partial z^3}$.

$$\frac{\partial^3 y}{\partial z^3} = \frac{\left(x^4 + 2x^2 z + z^2\right)(0) - (-1)\left(2x^2 + 2z\right)}{\left(x^4 + 2x^2 z + z^2\right)^2} - \frac{\left(x^2 - 2xz^2 + z^4\right)(4z) - \left(2x + 2z^2\right)\left(-4xz + 4z^3\right)}{\left(x^2 - 2xz^2 + z^4\right)^2}$$

$$\frac{\partial^3 y}{\partial z^3} = \frac{2x^2 + 2z}{\left(x^4 + 2x^2 z + z^2\right)^2} - \frac{4x^2 z - 8xz^3 + 4z^5 + 8x^2 z - 8xz^3 + 8xz^3 - 8z^5}{\left(x^2 - 2xz^2 + z^4\right)^2}$$

$$\frac{\partial^3 y}{\partial z^3} = \frac{2x^2 + 2z}{\left(x^4 + 2x^2 z + z^2\right)^2} - \frac{12x^2 z - 8xz^3 - 4z^5}{\left(x^2 - 2xz^2 + z^4\right)^2}$$

IMPLICIT DIFFERENTIATION

Implicitly differentiate each of the following.

1. $x^2 + y^2 = 6$

2. $3x + 7x^2 + y^3 = 8x^4$

3. $xy = 12x^2 + 11x$

4. $x^2 - 3y^2 = 8y + 10$

5. $\sin x + y^3 = \tan x$

6. $x^3 y^2 + 5y^4 = 16$

7. $y^8 + \cos x = e^{2x}$

8. $\left(4x - y^2\right)^3 = e^x$

9. $e^{xy} + y^3 = \sin xy$

10. $\dfrac{2}{y^3} + \sqrt{y} = 10x$

Answer Key

1. $\dfrac{dy}{dx} = -\dfrac{x}{y}$

2. $\dfrac{dy}{dx} = \dfrac{32x^3 - 14x - 3}{3y^2}$

3. $\dfrac{dy}{dx} = \dfrac{11}{x} - \dfrac{y}{x} + 24$

4. $\dfrac{dy}{dx} = \dfrac{x}{4 + 3y}$

5. $\dfrac{dy}{dx} = \dfrac{\sec^2 x - \cos x}{3y^2}$

6. $\dfrac{dy}{dx} = -\dfrac{3x^2 y}{2x^3 + 20y^2}$

7. $\dfrac{dy}{dx} = \dfrac{2e^{2x} + \sin x}{8y^7}$

8. $\dfrac{dy}{dx} = \dfrac{2}{y} - \dfrac{e^x}{6y\left(4x - y^2\right)^2}$

9. $\dfrac{dy}{dx} = \dfrac{y \cos xy - ye^{xy}}{xe^{xy} + 3y^2 - x \cos xy}$

10. $\dfrac{dy}{dx} = \dfrac{10}{\dfrac{-6}{y^4} + \dfrac{1}{2\sqrt{y}}}$

Solutions

1. $x^2 + y^2 = 6$

   Taking the derivative of each term, remembering to attach $\frac{dy}{dx}$ if we take a derivative of y, we get:

   $$2x + 2y\frac{dy}{dx} = 0$$

   Solving for $\frac{dy}{dx}$:

   $$2x + 2y\frac{dy}{dx} = 0$$

   $$2y\frac{dy}{dx} = -2x$$

   $$y\frac{dy}{dx} = -x$$

   $$\frac{dy}{dx} = -\frac{x}{y}$$

2. $3x + 7x^2 + y^3 = 8x^4$

   Taking the derivative of each term, remembering to attach $\frac{dy}{dx}$ if we take a derivative of y, we get:

   $$3 + 14x + 3y^2\frac{dy}{dx} = 32x^3$$

   Solving for $\frac{dy}{dx}$:

   $$3 + 14x + 3y^2\frac{dy}{dx} = 32x^3$$

   $$3y^2\frac{dy}{dx} = 32x^3 - 14x - 3$$

   $$\frac{dy}{dx} = \frac{32x^3 - 14x - 3}{3y^2}$$

3. $xy = 12x^2 + 11x$

Taking the derivative of each term, remembering to attach $\dfrac{dy}{dx}$ if we take a derivative of y, we get:

$$x\frac{dy}{dx} + y(1) = 24x + 11$$

Notice that we used the Product Rule to find the derivative of the product on the left-hand side since both terms in the product are functions of x.

Solving for $\dfrac{dy}{dx}$:

$$x\frac{dy}{dx} + y = 24x + 11$$

$$x\frac{dy}{dx} = 24x + 11 - y$$

$$\frac{dy}{dx} = \frac{24x + 11 - y}{x}$$

$$\frac{dy}{dx} = \frac{11}{x} - \frac{y}{x} + 24$$

4. $x^2 - 3y^2 = 8y + 10$

Taking the derivative of each term, remembering to attach $\dfrac{dy}{dx}$ if we take a derivative of y, we get:

$$2x - 6y\frac{dy}{dx} = 8\frac{dy}{dx}$$

Solving for $\dfrac{dy}{dx}$:

$$2x - 6y\frac{dy}{dx} = 8\frac{dy}{dx}$$

$$8\frac{dy}{dx} + 6y\frac{dy}{dx} = 2x$$

$$4\frac{dy}{dx} + 3y\frac{dy}{dx} = x$$

$$\frac{dy}{dx}(4 + 3y) = x$$

$$\frac{dy}{dx} = \frac{x}{4 + 3y}$$

5. $\sin x + y^3 = \tan x$

Taking the derivative of each term, remembering to attach $\dfrac{dy}{dx}$ if we take a derivative of y, we get:

$$\cos x + 3y^2\,\frac{dy}{dx} = \sec^2 x$$

Solving for $\dfrac{dy}{dx}$:

$$\cos x + 3y^2\,\frac{dy}{dx} = \sec^2 x$$

$$3y^2\,\frac{dy}{dx} = \sec^2 x - \cos x$$

$$\frac{dy}{dx} = \frac{\sec^2 x - \cos x}{3y^2}$$

6. $x^3 y^2 + 5y^4 = 16$

Taking the derivative of each term, remembering to attach $\dfrac{dy}{dx}$ if we take a derivative of y, we get:

$$x^3\left(2y\,\frac{dy}{dx}\right) + y^2\left(3x^2\right) + 20y^3\,\frac{dy}{dx} = 0$$

Notice that we used the Product Rule to find the derivative of the product on the left-hand side since both terms in the product are functions of x.

Solving for $\dfrac{dy}{dx}$:

$$x^3\left(2y\,\frac{dy}{dx}\right) + y^2\left(3x^2\right) + 20y^3\,\frac{dy}{dx} = 0$$

$$2x^3 y\,\frac{dy}{dx} + 3x^2 y^2 + 20y^3\,\frac{dy}{dx} = 0$$

$$2x^3 y\,\frac{dy}{dx} + 20y^3\,\frac{dy}{dx} = -3x^2 y^2$$

Factoring off y from each term:

$$2x^3\,\frac{dy}{dx} + 20y^2\,\frac{dy}{dx} = -3x^2 y$$

$$\frac{dy}{dx}\left(2x^3 + 20y^2\right) = -3x^2 y$$

$$\frac{dy}{dx} = -\frac{3x^2 y}{2x^3 + 20y^2}$$

7. $y^8 + \cos x = e^{2x}$

Taking the derivative of each term, remembering to attach $\dfrac{dy}{dx}$ if we take a derivative of y, we get:

$$8y^7 \frac{dy}{dx} - \sin x = 2e^{2x}$$

Solving for $\dfrac{dy}{dx}$:

$$8y^7 \frac{dy}{dx} - \sin x = 2e^{2x}$$

$$8y^7 \frac{dy}{dx} = 2e^{2x} + \sin x$$

$$\frac{dy}{dx} = \frac{2e^{2x} + \sin x}{8y^7}$$

8. $\left(4x - y^2\right)^3 = e^x$

Using the Power Rule on the left side of the equation, we find the derivative of each side of the equation:

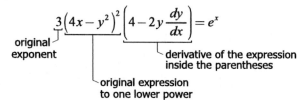

original exponent

original expression to one lower power

derivative of the expression inside the parentheses

Solving for $\dfrac{dy}{dx}$:

$$3\left(4x - y^2\right)^2 \left(4 - 2y\frac{dy}{dx}\right) = e^x$$

$$4 - 2y\frac{dy}{dx} = \frac{e^x}{3\left(4x - y^2\right)^2}$$

$$-2y\frac{dy}{dx} = \frac{e^x}{3\left(4x - y^2\right)^2} - 4$$

$$\frac{dy}{dx} = \frac{\dfrac{e^x}{3\left(4x - y^2\right)^2} - 4}{-2y}$$

$$\frac{dy}{dx} = \frac{-4}{-2y} + \frac{\dfrac{e^x}{3\left(4x - y^2\right)^2}}{-2y}$$

$$\frac{dy}{dx} = \frac{2}{y} - \frac{e^x}{6y\left(4x - y^2\right)^2}$$

9. $e^{xy} + y^3 = \sin xy$

Notice that when taking the derivative of e^{xy} and $\sin xy$ we must use the Product Rule as part of the process.

Taking the derivative of each term, remembering to attach $\dfrac{dy}{dx}$ if we take a derivative of y, we get:

$$\left[x\frac{dy}{dx} + y(1) \right] e^{xy} + 3y^2 \frac{dy}{dx} = \left[x\frac{dy}{dx} + y(1) \right] \cos xy$$

Solving for $\dfrac{dy}{dx}$:

$$xe^{xy} \frac{dy}{dx} + ye^{xy} + 3y^2 \frac{dy}{dx} = x(\cos xy)\frac{dy}{dx} + y\cos xy$$

$$xe^{xy} \frac{dy}{dx} + 3y^2 \frac{dy}{dx} - x(\cos xy)\frac{dy}{dx} = y\cos xy - ye^{xy}$$

$$\frac{dy}{dx}\left(xe^{xy} + 3y^2 - x\cos xy \right) = y\cos xy - ye^{xy}$$

$$\frac{dy}{dx} = \frac{y\cos xy - ye^{xy}}{xe^{xy} + 3y^2 - x\cos xy}$$

10. $\dfrac{2}{y^3} + \sqrt{y} = 10x$

$2y^{-3} + y^{\frac{1}{2}} = 10x$

Taking the derivative of each term, remembering to attach $\dfrac{dy}{dx}$ if we take a derivative of y, we get:

$$-6y^{-4}\frac{dy}{dx} + \frac{1}{2}y^{-\frac{1}{2}}\frac{dy}{dx} = 10$$

Solving for $\dfrac{dy}{dx}$:

$$\frac{-6}{y^4}\frac{dy}{dx} + \frac{1}{2\sqrt{y}}\frac{dy}{dx} = 10$$

$$\frac{dy}{dx}\left(\frac{-6}{y^4} + \frac{1}{2\sqrt{y}} \right) = 10$$

$$\frac{dy}{dx} = \frac{10}{\dfrac{-6}{y^4} + \dfrac{1}{2\sqrt{y}}}$$

Find any/all maxima, minima, and points of inflection for each of the following.

1. $f(x) = x^2$

2. $f(x) = -x^2$

3. $f(x) = x^3$

4. $f(x) = \dfrac{1}{3}x^3 - \dfrac{1}{2}x^2 - 6x + 5$

5. $f(x) = 3x^2 + x$

6. $f(x) = \dfrac{1}{4}x^4 - \dfrac{7}{2}x^2 + 6x + 10$

7. $f(x) = -(x+2)^3$

8. $f(x) = \sin x$

9. $f(x) = \tan x$

10. $f(x) = -(x-1)^2 + 2x$

Solutions

1. $f(x) = x^2$

To find the points of interest, we take the first derivative, 1), set the resulting expression equal to zero, 2), and solve the resulting equation, 3).

1) $f(x) = x^2$

   $f'(x) = 2x$

2) $2x = 0$

3) $\dfrac{2x}{2} = \dfrac{0}{2}$

   $x = 0$

Point of interest: $x = 0$

To see if a point of interest is a possible maximum, minimum, or point of inflection, we now take the second derivative and evaluate the second derivative at the point of interest.

$f'(x) = 2x$

$f''(x) = 2 \qquad \Rightarrow \quad f''(0) = 2$

Since the 2nd derivative is positive at the point of interest, it is a relative minimum for the function.

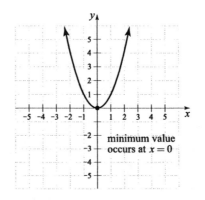

minimum value
occurs at $x = 0$

2. $f(x) = -x^2$

To find the points of interest, we take the first derivative, 1), set the resulting expression equal to zero, 2), and solve the resulting equation, 3).

1) $f'(x) = -2x$

2) $-2x = 0$

3) $\dfrac{-2x}{-2} = \dfrac{0}{-2}$

$x = 0$

Point of interest: $x = 0$

To see if a point of interest is a possible maximum, minimum, or point of inflection, we now take the second derivative and evaluate the second derivative at the point of interest.

$f'(x) = -2x$

$f''(x) = -2 \quad \Rightarrow \quad f''(0) = -2$

Since the 2nd derivative is negative at the point of interest, it is a relative maximum for the function.

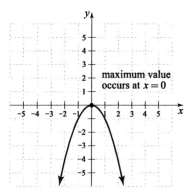

3. $f(x) = x^3$

To find the points of interest, we take the first derivative, 1), set the resulting expression equal to zero, 2), and solve the resulting equation, 3).

1) $f'(x) = 3x^2$

2) $3x^2 = 0$

3) $3x^2 = 0$

$$\frac{3x^2}{3} = \frac{0}{3}$$

$$x^2 = 0$$

$$\sqrt{x^2} = \sqrt{0}$$

$$x = 0$$

Point of interest: $x = 0$

To see if a point of interest is a possible maximum, minimum, or point of inflection, we now take the second derivative and evaluate the second derivative at the point of interest.

$$f'(x) = 3x^2$$

$$f''(x) = 6x \quad \Rightarrow \quad f''(0) = 6(0) = 0$$

Since the second derivative is zero at the point of interest it is a potential point of inflection. To test it, we must test the sign of the second derivative on either side of the point. Choosing $x = -0.1$ and $x = 0.1$:

$$f''(x) = 6x$$

$$f''(-0.1) = 6(-0.1) = -0.6$$

$$f''(0.1) = 6(0.1) = 0.6$$

Since the signs of the second derivatives are different, the point $x = 0$ is indeed a point of inflection for the function $f(x) = x^3$.

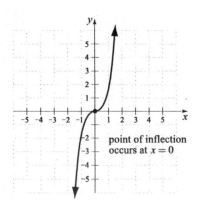

point of inflection occurs at $x = 0$

4. $f(x) = \dfrac{1}{3}x^3 - \dfrac{1}{2}x^2 - 6x + 5$

To find the points of interest, we take the first derivative, 1), set the resulting expression equal to zero, 2), and solve the resulting equation, 3).

1) $f'(x) = x^2 - x - 6$

2) $x^2 - x - 6 = 0$

3) $x^2 - x - 6 = 0$

   Factoring:

   $(x-3)(x+2) = 0$

   $x - 3 = 0 \qquad x + 2 = 0$

   $x = 3 \qquad x = -2$

Points of interest: $x = 3, x = -2$

Next, we calculate the second derivative and evaluate it at each of the point of interest.

$f''(x) = 2x - 1$

$f''(3) = 2(3) - 1 = 6 - 1 = 5$

$f''(-2) = 2(-2) - 1 = -4 - 1 = -5$

Since $f''(3) > 0$ it is a relative minimum for the function. Likewise, since $f''(-2) < 0$ it is a relative maximum for the function.

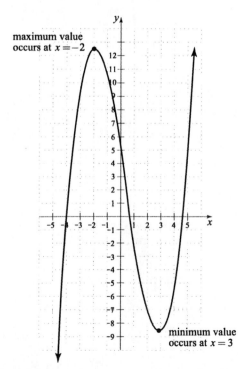

maximum value
occurs at $x = -2$

minimum value
occurs at $x = 3$

5. $f(x) = 3x^2 + x$

To find the points of interest, we take the first derivative, 1), set the resulting expression equal to zero, 2), and solve the resulting equation, 3).

1) $f(x) = 3x^2 + x$

$f'(x) = 6x + 1$

2) $6x + 1 = 0$

3) $6x + 1 = 0$

$6x = -1$

$x = -\dfrac{1}{6}$

Point of interest: $x = -\dfrac{1}{6}$

To see if a point of interest is a possible maximum, minimum, or point of inflection, we now take the second derivative and evaluate the second derivative at the point of interest.

$f'(x) = 6x + 1$

$f''(x) = 6 \qquad \Rightarrow \quad f''\left(-\dfrac{1}{6}\right) = 6$

Since the 2nd derivative is positive at the point of interest, a relative minimum occurs at $x = -\dfrac{1}{6}$.

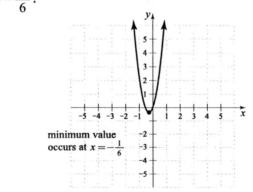

minimum value
occurs at $x = -\dfrac{1}{6}$

6. $f(x) = \dfrac{1}{4}x^4 - \dfrac{7}{2}x^2 + 6x + 10$

To find the points of interest, we take the first derivative, 1), set the resulting expression equal to zero, 2), and solve the resulting equation, 3).

1) $f(x) = \dfrac{1}{4}x^4 - \dfrac{7}{2}x^2 + 6x + 10$

$f'(x) = x^3 - 7x + 6$

calculation cont. on next page...

Solution #6 from previous page...

2) $x^3 - 7x + 6 = 0$

3) $x^3 - 7x + 6 = 0$

Factoring:

$(x-1)(x-2)(x+3) = 0$

Setting each factor equal to zero we find the points of interest:

$x - 1 = 0$ $x - 2 = 0$ $x + 3 = 0$

$x = 1$ $x = 2$ $x = -3$

Points of interest: $x = 1, x = 2, x = -3$

To see if a point of interest is a possible maximum, minimum, or point of inflection, we now take the second derivative and evaluate the second derivative at the point of interest.

$f'(x) = x^3 - 7x + 6$

$f''(x) = 3x^2 - 7$

$f''(1) = 3(1)^2 - 7 = -4 < 0$ $\Rightarrow$ a relative maximum occurs at $x = 1$

$f''(2) = 3(2)^2 - 7 = 5 > 0$ $\Rightarrow$ a relative minimum occurs at $x = 2$

$f''(-3) = 3(-3)^2 - 7 = 20 > 0$ $\Rightarrow$ a relative minimum occurs at $x = -3$

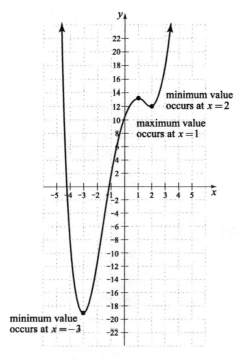

7. $f(x) = -(x+2)^3$

To find the points of interest, we take the first derivative, 1), set the resulting expression equal to zero, 2), and solve the resulting equation, 3).

1) $f(x) = -(x+2)^3$

$f'(x) = -3(x+2)^2 (1) = -3(x+2)^2$

2) $-3(x+2)^2 = 0$

3) $-3(x+2)^2 = 0$

$\dfrac{-3(x+2)^2}{-3} = \dfrac{0}{-3}$

$(x+2)^2 = 0$

$\sqrt{(x+2)^2} = \sqrt{0}$

$x+2 = 0$

$x = -2$

Point of interest: $x = -2$

To see if a point of interest is a possible maximum, minimum, or point of inflection, we now take the second derivative and evaluate the second derivative at the point of interest.

$f'(x) = -3(x+2)^2$

$f''(x) = -6(x+2)^1 (1)$

$f''(x) = -6x - 12$

$f''(-2) = -6(-2) - 12 = 12 - 12 = 0$

Since the second derivative is zero at the point of interest it is a potential point of inflection. To test it, we must test the sign of the second derivative on either side of the point. Choosing $x = -2.1$ and $x = 1.9$:

$f''(x) = -6x - 12$

$f''(-2.1) = -6(-2.1) - 12 = 12.6 - 12 = 0.6$

$f''(-1.9) = -6(-1.9) - 12 = 11.4 - 12 = -0.6$

calculation cont. on next page...

Solution #7 from previous page...

Since the signs of the second derivatives are different, the point $x = -2$ is indeed a point of inflection for the function $f(x) = -(x+2)^3$

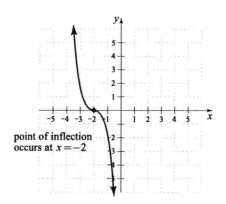

point of inflection occurs at $x = -2$

8. $f(x) = \sin x$

To find the points of interest, we take the first derivative, 1), set the resulting expression equal to zero, 2), and solve the resulting equation, 3).

1) $f(x) = \sin x$

$f'(x) = \cos x$

2) $\cos x = 0$

3) The cosine function is equal to zero at all odd integer multiples of $\dfrac{\pi}{2}$.

Consequently, each of these points is a point of interest for the function $f(x) = \sin x$.

To decide which points are maxima and which points are minima (beyond simply looking at the graph), we take the 2nd derivative of the function and evaluate its signs at the points of interest.

$f'(x) = \cos x$

$f''(x) = -\sin x$

Since the 2nd derivative is negative at 2π increments of $\dfrac{\pi}{2}$, relative maxima occur at each of these points:

$f''\left(\dfrac{\pi}{2}\right) = -\sin\dfrac{\pi}{2} = -1$

$f''\left(\dfrac{5\pi}{2}\right) = -\sin\dfrac{5\pi}{2} = -1$

$f''\left(\dfrac{9\pi}{2}\right) = -\sin\dfrac{9\pi}{2} = -1$

calculation cont. on next page...

Solution #8 from previous page...

Since the 2nd derivative is positive at 2π increments of $\dfrac{3\pi}{2}$, relative minima occur at each of these points:

$$f''\left(\frac{3\pi}{2}\right) = -\sin\frac{3\pi}{2} = -(-1) = 1$$

$$f''\left(\frac{7\pi}{2}\right) = -\sin\frac{7\pi}{2} = -(-1) = 1$$

$$f''\left(\frac{11\pi}{2}\right) = -\sin\frac{11\pi}{2} = -(-1) = 1$$

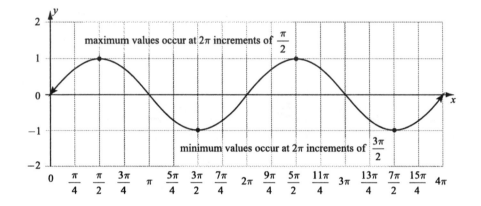

9. $f(x) = \tan x$

To find the points of interest, we take the first derivative, 1), set the resulting expression equal to zero, 2), and solve the resulting equation, 3).

1) $f(x) = \tan x$

$f'(x) = \sec^2 x$

2) $\sec^2 x = 0$

3) The secant function is equal to zero at 2π increments of π.

Consequently, each of these points is a point of interest for the function $f(x) = \tan x$.

To identify the points of interest as maxima, minima, or points of inflection, we evaluate the 2nd derivative at the points of interest.

$f'(x) = \sec^2 x$

$f''(x) = (2\sec x)(\sec x \tan x) = \left(2 \cdot \dfrac{1}{\cos x}\right)\left(\dfrac{1}{\cos x} \cdot \dfrac{\sin x}{\cos x}\right) = \dfrac{2\sin x}{\cos^3 x}$

calculation cont. on next page...

Solution #9 from previous page...

Since the numerator of the 2nd derivative yields zero at each point of interest while the denominator is -1, the 2nd derivative is equal to zero at each of the points of interest.

$$f''(\pi) = \frac{2 \sin \pi}{\cos^3 \pi} = \frac{2(0)}{-1} = 0$$

$$f''(3\pi) = \frac{2 \sin 3\pi}{\cos^3 3\pi} = \frac{2(0)}{-1} = 0$$

$$f''(5\pi) = \frac{2 \sin 5\pi}{\cos^3 5\pi} = \frac{2(0)}{-1} = 0$$

Consequently, each of the points of interest is a potential point of inflection. To decide if the points are indeed points of inflection, we evaluate the 2nd derivative at a point to the left and a point to the right of the point of interest.

Point to the left of the point of interest:

$$f''\left(\frac{3\pi}{4}\right) = \frac{2 \sin \dfrac{3\pi}{4}}{\cos^3 \dfrac{3\pi}{4}} = \frac{2\left(\dfrac{\sqrt{2}}{2}\right)}{\left(-\dfrac{\sqrt{2}}{2}\right)^3} < 0$$

Point to the right of the point of interest:

$$f''\left(\frac{3\pi}{4}\right) = \frac{2 \sin \dfrac{5\pi}{4}}{\cos^3 \dfrac{5\pi}{4}} = \frac{2\left(-\dfrac{\sqrt{2}}{2}\right)}{\left(-\dfrac{\sqrt{2}}{2}\right)^3} > 0$$

calculation cont. on next page...

Solution #9 from previous page...

Since the sign of the second derivative changes as we move from the left to the right of a point of interest, the point is indeed a point of inflection.

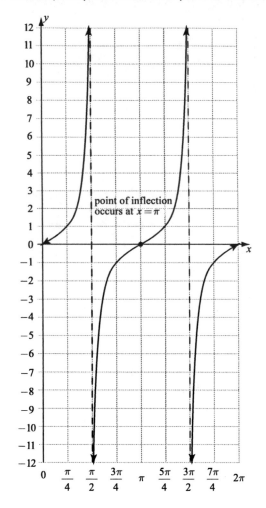

point of inflection occurs at $x = \pi$

10. $f(x) = -(x-1)^2 + 2x$

To find the points of interest, we take the first derivative, 1), set the resulting expression equal to zero, 2), and solve the resulting equation, 3).

1) $f(x) = -(x-1)^2 + 2x$

     $f'(x) = -2(x-1)^1(1) + 2 = -2x + 2 + 2 = -2x + 4$

2) $-2x + 4 = 0$

3) $-2x + 4 = 0$

     $-2x = -4$

     $\dfrac{-2x}{-2} = \dfrac{-4}{-2}$

     $x = 2$

Point of interest: $x = 2$

To see if a point of interest is a possible maximum, minimum, or point of inflection, we now take the second derivative and evaluate the second derivative at the point of interest.

$f'(x) = -2x + 4$

$f''(x) = -2 \quad \Rightarrow \quad f''(-2) = -2 < 0$

Since the sign of the 2nd derivative is negative at the point of interest, the function achieves a relative maximum at $x = 2$.

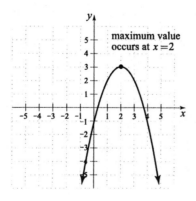

maximum value occurs at $x = 2$

INDEFINITE INTEGRALS

Integrate each of the following. Remember to attach a C to your answer, indicating a possible unknown constant of integration.

1. $\displaystyle\int 2x\,dx$

2. $\displaystyle\int x^2\,dx$

3. $\displaystyle\int x^3\,dx$

4. $\displaystyle\int 3\,dx$

5. $\displaystyle\int 12\,dx$

6. $\displaystyle\int \frac{1}{2}x\,dx$

7. $\displaystyle\int \left(x^2 + 4x\right)dx$

8. $\displaystyle\int \left(x^3 - x^2 + 6x\right)dx$

9. $\displaystyle\int \sqrt{x}\,dx$

10. $\displaystyle\int \left(\frac{x}{3} - \frac{x^2}{4}\right)dx$

11. $\displaystyle\int \frac{2}{x^3}\,dx$

12. $\displaystyle\int \left(\frac{5}{x^4} - \sqrt[3]{x}\right)dx$

13. $\displaystyle\int 2.5x\,dx$

14. $\displaystyle\int \frac{5}{\sqrt{x}}\,dx$

15. $\displaystyle\int \left(\frac{1}{x^5} + \frac{\sqrt[4]{x}}{2} + 10\right)dx$

Answer Key

1. $x^2 + C$

2. $\dfrac{1}{3}x^3 + C$

3. $\dfrac{1}{4}x^4 + C$

4. $3x + C$

5. $12x + C$

6. $\dfrac{1}{4}x^2 + C$

7. $\dfrac{1}{3}x^3 + 2x^2 + C$

8. $\dfrac{1}{4}x^4 - \dfrac{1}{3}x^3 + 3x^2 + C$

9. $\dfrac{2}{3}x\sqrt{x} + C$

10. $\dfrac{1}{6}x^2 - \dfrac{1}{12}x^3 + C$

11. $-\dfrac{1}{x^2} + C$

12. $-\dfrac{5}{3x^3} - \dfrac{3}{4}x\sqrt[3]{x} + C$

13. $1.25x^2 + C$

14. $10\sqrt{x} + C$

15. $-\dfrac{1}{4x^4} + \dfrac{2}{5}x\sqrt[4]{x} + 10x + C$

Solutions

1. $\int 2x\,dx$

   Raising the exponent on x by 1 and then multiplying in front by 1 divided by the *new* exponent we get:

   $$\int 2x^1\,dx = 2\left(\frac{1}{2}\right)x^2 + C = x^2 + C$$

2. $\int x^2\,dx$

   Raising the exponent on x by 1 and then multiplying in front by 1 divided by the *new* exponent we get:

   $$\int x^2\,dx = \frac{1}{3}x^3 + C$$

3. $\int x^3\,dx$

   Raising the exponent on x by 1 and then multiplying in front by 1 divided by the *new* exponent we get:

   $$\int x^3\,dx = \frac{1}{4}x^4 + C$$

4. $\int 3\,dx$

   Since $x^0 = 1$, we can rewrite the integral as:

   $$\int 3\,dx = \int 3x^0\,dx$$

   Raising the exponent on x by 1 and then multiplying in front by 1 divided by the *new* exponent we get:

   $$\int 3x^0\,dx = 3\left(\frac{1}{1}\right)x^1 + C = 3x + C$$

5. $\int 12\,dx$

   Since $x^0 = 1$, we can rewrite the integral as:

   $$\int 12\,dx = \int 12x^0\,dx$$

   Raising the exponent on x by 1 and then multiplying in front by 1 divided by the *new* exponent we get:

   $$\int 12x^0\,dx = 12\left(\frac{1}{1}\right)x^1 + C = 12x + C$$

Notes

6. $\int \dfrac{1}{2} x\, dx$

Raising the exponent on x by 1 and then multiplying in front by 1 divided by the *new* exponent we get:

$$\int \frac{1}{2} x\, dx = \frac{1}{2}\left(\frac{1}{2}\right)x^2 + C = \frac{1}{4}x^2 + C$$

7. $\int \left(x^2 + 4x\right) dx$

Integrating each of the terms separately:

$$\int \left(x^2 + 4x\right) dx = \frac{1}{3}x^3 + 4\left(\frac{1}{2}\right)x^2 + C = \frac{1}{3}x^3 + 2x^2 + C$$

8. $\int \left(x^3 - x^2 + 6x\right) dx$

Integrating each of the terms separately:

$$\int \left(x^3 - x^2 + 6x\right) dx = \frac{1}{4}x^4 - \frac{1}{3}x^3 + 6\left(\frac{1}{2}\right)x^2 + C$$

$$= \frac{1}{4}x^4 - \frac{1}{3}x^3 + 3x^2 + C$$

9. $\int \sqrt{x}\, dx = \int x^{\frac{1}{2}}\, dx$

Raising the exponent on x by 1 and then multiplying in front by 1 divided by the *new* exponent we get:

$$\int x^{\frac{1}{2}}\, dx = \frac{1}{\frac{3}{2}} x^{\frac{3}{2}} + C = \frac{2}{3} x^{\frac{3}{2}} + C = \frac{2}{3} x\sqrt{x} + C$$

10. $\int \left(\dfrac{x}{3} - \dfrac{x^2}{4}\right) dx = \int \left(\dfrac{1}{3}x - \dfrac{1}{4}x^2\right) dx$

Integrating each of the terms separately:

$$\int \left(\frac{1}{3}x - \frac{1}{4}x^2\right) dx = \frac{1}{3}\left(\frac{1}{2}\right)x^2 - \frac{1}{4}\left(\frac{1}{3}\right)x^3 + C$$

$$= \frac{1}{6}x^2 - \frac{1}{12}x^3 + C$$

11. $\int \dfrac{2}{x^3}\, dx = \int 2x^{-3}\, dx$

Raising the exponent on x by 1 and then multiplying in front by 1 divided by the *new* exponent we get:

$$\int 2x^{-3}\, dx = 2\left(\frac{1}{-2}\right)x^{-2} + C = -x^{-2} + C = -\frac{1}{x^2} + C$$

12. $\int \left(\dfrac{5}{x^4} - \sqrt[3]{x} \right) dx = \int \left(5x^{-4} - x^{\frac{1}{3}} \right) dx$

Integrating each of the terms separately:

$$\int \left(5x^{-4} - x^{\frac{1}{3}} \right) dx = 5 \left(\dfrac{1}{-3} \right) x^{-3} - \dfrac{1}{\frac{4}{3}} x^{\frac{4}{3}} + C$$

$$= -\dfrac{5}{3} x^{-3} - \dfrac{3}{4} x^{\frac{4}{3}} + C$$

$$= -\dfrac{5}{3x^3} - \dfrac{3}{4} x \sqrt[3]{x} + C$$

13. $\int 2.5x\,dx$

Raising the exponent on x by 1 and then multiplying in front by 1 divided by the *new* exponent we get:

$$\int 2.5x\,dx = 2.5 \left(\dfrac{1}{2} \right) x^2 + C = 1.25x^2 + C$$

14. $\int \dfrac{5}{\sqrt{x}}\,dx = \int \dfrac{5}{x^{\frac{1}{2}}}\,dx = \int 5x^{-\frac{1}{2}}\,dx$

Raising the exponent on x by 1 and then multiplying in front by 1 divided by the *new* exponent we get:

$$\int 5x^{-\frac{1}{2}}\,dx = 5 \left(\dfrac{1}{\frac{1}{2}} \right) x^{\frac{1}{2}} + C = 5(2) x^{\frac{1}{2}} + C = 10\sqrt{x} + C$$

15. $\int \left(\dfrac{1}{x^5} + \dfrac{\sqrt[4]{x}}{2} + 10 \right) dx = \int \left(x^{-5} + \dfrac{1}{2} x^{\frac{1}{4}} + 10 \right) dx$

Integrating each of the terms separately:

$$\int \left(x^{-5} + \dfrac{1}{2} x^{\frac{1}{4}} + 10 \right) dx = \dfrac{1}{-4} x^{-4} + \dfrac{1}{2} \left(\dfrac{1}{\frac{5}{4}} \right) x^{\frac{5}{4}} + 10x + C$$

$$= -\dfrac{1}{4x^4} + \dfrac{1}{2} \left(\dfrac{4}{5} \right) x^{\frac{5}{4}} + 10x + C$$

$$= -\dfrac{1}{4x^4} + \dfrac{2}{5} x \sqrt[4]{x} + 10x + C$$

DEFINITE
INTEGRALS

Evaluate each of the following.

1. $\displaystyle\int_{0}^{1} x^2\, dx$

2. $\displaystyle\int_{-2}^{1} 5x\, dx$

3. $\displaystyle\int_{0}^{2} \left(3x^2 + 4\right) dx$

4. $\displaystyle\int_{-2}^{0} \left(x + 5\right) dx$

5. $\displaystyle\int_{1}^{4} \sqrt{x}\, dx$

6. $\displaystyle\int_{4}^{9} \frac{2}{\sqrt{x}}\, dx$

7. $\displaystyle\int_{1.1}^{1.5} dx$

8. $\displaystyle\int_{-3}^{3} \frac{1}{3} x^2\, dx$

9. $\displaystyle\int_{1}^{8} 5\sqrt[3]{x}\, dx$

10. $\displaystyle\int_{-3}^{1} \left(x^2 + x + 2\right) dx$

11. $\displaystyle\int_{0}^{1} e^x\, dx$

12. $\displaystyle\int_{1}^{2} 2e^{2x}\, dx$

13. $\displaystyle\int_{0}^{\frac{\pi}{2}} \cos x\, dx$

14. $\displaystyle\int_{0}^{\pi} 2\sin x\, dx$

15. $\displaystyle\int_{2}^{3} \frac{x^2 - 4}{x + 2}\, dx$

16. $\displaystyle\int_{0}^{1} \left(x + e^x\right) dx$

17. $\displaystyle\int_{0}^{\frac{\pi}{4}} \left(3\sin x + \cos x\right) dx$

18. $\displaystyle\int_{2}^{4} \left(\frac{4}{x^2} + 8\right) dx$

19. $\displaystyle\int_{1}^{9} \left(\frac{\sqrt{x}}{3} + \frac{5}{\sqrt{x}}\right) dx$

20. $\displaystyle\int_{0}^{\frac{\pi}{4}} 6\sec^2 x\, dx$

Notes

Answer Key

1. $\displaystyle\int_0^1 x^2\,dx = \dfrac{1}{3}$

2. $\displaystyle\int_{-2}^1 5x\,dx = -7\dfrac{1}{2}$

3. $\displaystyle\int_0^2 \left(3x^2 + 4\right)dx = 16$

4. $\displaystyle\int_{-2}^0 (x+5)\,dx = 8$

5. $\displaystyle\int_1^4 \sqrt{x}\,dx = 4\dfrac{2}{3}$

6. $\displaystyle\int_4^9 \dfrac{2}{\sqrt{x}}\,dx = 4$

7. $\displaystyle\int_{1.1}^{1.5} dx = 0.4$

8. $\displaystyle\int_{-3}^3 \dfrac{1}{3}x^2\,dx = 54$

9. $\displaystyle\int_1^8 5\sqrt[3]{x}\,dx = 56\dfrac{1}{4}$

10. $\displaystyle\int_{-3}^1 \left(x^2 + x + 2\right)dx = 26\dfrac{2}{3}$

11. $\displaystyle\int_0^1 e^x\,dx = e - 1$

12. $\displaystyle\int_1^2 2e^{2x}\,dx = e^4 - e^2$

13. $\displaystyle\int_0^{\frac{\pi}{2}} \cos x\,dx = 1$

14. $\displaystyle\int_0^{\pi} 2\sin x\,dx = 4$

15. $\displaystyle\int_2^3 \dfrac{x^2 - 4}{x+2}\,dx = \dfrac{1}{2}$

16. $\displaystyle\int_0^1 \left(x + e^x\right)dx = e - \dfrac{1}{2}$

17. $\displaystyle\int_0^{\frac{\pi}{4}} \left(3\sin x + \cos x\right)dx = 3 - \sqrt{2}$

18. $\displaystyle\int_2^4 \left(\dfrac{4}{x^2} + 8\right)dx = 17$

19. $\displaystyle\int_1^9 \left(\dfrac{\sqrt{x}}{3} + \dfrac{5}{\sqrt{x}}\right)dx = 25\dfrac{7}{9}$

20. $\displaystyle\int_0^{\frac{\pi}{4}} 6\sec^2 x\,dx = 6$

Solutions

1. $\displaystyle\int_0^1 x^2\,dx = \left[\frac{1}{3}x^3\right]_0^1$

$\qquad = \frac{1}{3}(1)^3 - \frac{1}{3}(0)^3$

$\qquad = \frac{1}{3} - 0$

$\qquad = \frac{1}{3}$

2. $\displaystyle\int_{-2}^1 5x\,dx = \left[\frac{5}{2}x^2\right]_{-2}^1$

$\qquad = \frac{5}{2}(1)^2 - \frac{5}{2}(-2)^2$

$\qquad = \frac{5}{2} - 10$

$\qquad = -7\frac{1}{2}$

3. $\displaystyle\int_0^2 \left(3x^2 + 4\right)dx = \left[x^3 + 4x\right]_0^2$

$\qquad = \left[2^3 + 4(2)\right] - \left[0^3 + 4(0)\right]$

$\qquad = 8 + 8 - 0$

$\qquad = 16$

4. $\displaystyle\int_{-2}^0 (x+5)\,dx = \left[\frac{1}{2}x^2 + 5x\right]_{-2}^0$

$\qquad = \left[\frac{1}{2}(0)^2 + 5(0)\right] - \left[\frac{1}{2}(-2)^2 + 5(-2)\right]$

$\qquad = 0 - (2 - 10)$

$\qquad = -(-8)$

$\qquad = 8$

5. $\displaystyle\int_1^4 \sqrt{x}\, dx = \int_1^4 x^{\frac{1}{2}}\, dx$

$$= \left[\frac{2}{3} x^{\frac{3}{2}}\right]_1^4$$

$$= \left[\frac{2}{3} x\sqrt{x}\right]_1^4$$

$$= \frac{2}{3}(4)\sqrt{4} - \frac{2}{3}(1)\sqrt{1}$$

$$= \frac{16}{3} - \frac{2}{3}$$

$$= \frac{14}{3}$$

$$= 4\frac{2}{3}$$

6. $\displaystyle\int_4^9 \frac{2}{\sqrt{x}}\, dx = \int_4^9 \frac{2}{x^{\frac{1}{2}}}\, dx = \int_4^9 2x^{-\frac{1}{2}}\, dx$

$$= \left[2\left(2x^{\frac{1}{2}}\right)\right]_4^9$$

$$= \left[4\sqrt{x}\right]_4^9$$

$$= 4\sqrt{9} - 4\sqrt{4}$$

$$= 12 - 8$$

$$= 4$$

7. $\displaystyle\int_{1.1}^{1.5} dx = \left[x\right]_{1.1}^{1.5} = 1.5 - 1.1 = 0.4$

8. $\displaystyle\int_{-3}^{3} \frac{1}{3} x^2\, dx = \left[x^3\right]_{-3}^{3} = 3^3 - (-3)^3 = 27 - (-27) = 54$

9. $\displaystyle\int_1^8 5\sqrt[3]{x}\,dx = \int_1^8 5\,x^{\frac{1}{3}}\,dx$

$$= \left[5\left(\frac{3}{4}x^{\frac{4}{3}}\right)\right]_1^8$$

$$= \left[\frac{15}{4}x\sqrt[3]{x}\right]_1^8$$

$$= \left[\frac{15}{4}(8)\sqrt[3]{8}\right] - \left[\frac{15}{4}(1)\sqrt[3]{1}\right]$$

$$= \left[30(2)\right] - \frac{15}{4}$$

$$= 60 - \frac{15}{4}$$

$$= \frac{225}{4} = 56\frac{1}{4}$$

10. $\displaystyle\int_{-3}^1 \left(x^2 + x + 2\right)dx = \left[\frac{1}{3}x^3 + \frac{1}{2}x^2 + 2x\right]_{-3}^1$

$$= \left[\frac{1}{3}(1)^3 + \frac{1}{2}(1)^2 + 2(1)\right] - \left[\frac{1}{3}(-3)^3 + \frac{1}{2}(-3)^2 + 2(-3)\right]$$

$$= \left[\frac{1}{3} + \frac{1}{2} + 2\right] - \left[-9 + \frac{9}{2} - 6\right]$$

$$= \left(\frac{17}{6}\right) - \left(-\frac{21}{2}\right)$$

$$= \frac{80}{6} = 26\frac{2}{3}$$

11. $\displaystyle\int_0^1 e^x\,dx = \left[e^x\right]_0^1 = e^1 - e^0 = e - 1$

12. $\displaystyle\int_1^2 2e^{2x}\,dx = \left[e^{2x}\right]_1^2 = e^{2(2)} - e^{2(1)} = e^4 - e^2$

13. $\displaystyle\int_0^{\frac{\pi}{2}} \cos x\,dx = \left[\sin x\right]_0^{\frac{\pi}{2}}$

$$= \sin\frac{\pi}{2} - \sin 0$$

$$= 1 - 0$$

$$= 1$$

14. $\displaystyle\int_0^\pi 2\sin x\,dx = \left[-2\cos x\right]_0^\pi$

$$= \left[-2\cos\pi\right]-\left[-2\cos 0\right]$$

$$= \left[-2(-1)\right]-\left[-2(1)\right]$$

$$= 2+2$$

$$= 4$$

15. $\displaystyle\int_2^3 \frac{x^2-4}{x+2}\,dx = \int_2^3 \frac{(x+2)(x-2)}{(x+2)}\,dx = \int_2^3 (x-2)\,dx$

$$= \left[\frac{1}{2}x^2 - 2x\right]_2^3$$

$$= \left[\frac{1}{2}(3)^2 - 2(3)\right]-\left[\frac{1}{2}(2)^2 - 2(2)\right]$$

$$= \left(\frac{9}{2}-6\right)-(2-4)$$

$$= -\frac{3}{2}+2$$

$$= \frac{1}{2}$$

16. $\displaystyle\int_0^1 \left(x+e^x\right)dx = \left[\frac{1}{2}x^2 + e^x\right]_0^1$

$$= \left[\frac{1}{2}(1)^2 + e^1\right]-\left[\frac{1}{2}(0)^2 + e^0\right]$$

$$= \left(\frac{1}{2}+e\right)-(0+1)$$

$$= \frac{1}{2}+e-1$$

$$= e-\frac{1}{2}$$

17. $\displaystyle\int_{0}^{\frac{\pi}{4}}\left(3\sin x+\cos x\right)dx=\left[-3\cos x+\sin x\right]_{0}^{\frac{\pi}{4}}$

$$=\left[-3\cos\frac{\pi}{4}+\sin\frac{\pi}{4}\right]-\left[-3\cos 0+\sin 0\right]$$

$$=\left[-3\cdot\frac{\sqrt{2}}{2}+\frac{\sqrt{2}}{2}\right]-\left[-3(1)+0\right]$$

$$=\left(-2\cdot\frac{\sqrt{2}}{2}\right)+3$$

$$=-\sqrt{2}+3$$

$$=3-\sqrt{2}$$

18. $\displaystyle\int_{2}^{4}\left(\frac{4}{x^{2}}+8\right)dx=\int_{2}^{4}\left(4x^{-2}+8\right)dx$

$$=\left[-4x^{-1}+8x\right]_{2}^{4}$$

$$=\left[-\frac{4}{x}+8x\right]_{2}^{4}$$

$$=\left[-\frac{4}{4}+8(4)\right]-\left[-\frac{4}{2}+8(2)\right]$$

$$=(-1+32)-(-2+16)$$

$$=31-14$$

$$=17$$

19. $\int_{1}^{9}\left(\frac{\sqrt{x}}{3}+\frac{5}{\sqrt{x}}\right)dx = \int_{1}^{9}\left(\frac{x^{\frac{1}{2}}}{3}+\frac{5}{x^{\frac{1}{2}}}\right)dx = \int_{1}^{9}\left(\frac{1}{3}x^{\frac{1}{2}}+5x^{-\frac{1}{2}}\right)dx$

$$= \left[\frac{1}{3}\left(\frac{2}{3}x^{\frac{3}{2}}\right)+5\left(2x^{\frac{1}{2}}\right)\right]_{1}^{9}$$

$$= \left[\frac{2}{9}x^{\frac{3}{2}}+10x^{\frac{1}{2}}\right]_{1}^{9}$$

$$= \left[\frac{2}{9}x\sqrt{x}+10\sqrt{x}\right]_{1}^{9}$$

$$= \left[\frac{2}{9}(9)\sqrt{9}+10\sqrt{9}\right]-\left[\frac{2}{9}(1)\sqrt{1}+10\sqrt{1}\right]$$

$$= \left[2(3)+10(3)\right]-\left[\frac{2}{9}+10\right]$$

$$= 36-\frac{92}{9}$$

$$= 25\frac{7}{9}$$

20. $\int_{0}^{\frac{\pi}{4}} 6\sec^2 x\,dx = \left[6\tan x\right]_{0}^{\frac{\pi}{4}}$

$$= 6\tan\frac{\pi}{4}-6\tan 0$$

$$= 6(1)-0$$

$$= 6$$

Integrate each of the following using the method of substitution.

1. $\displaystyle \int 2x\left(x^2 - 5\right)^6 dx$

2. $\displaystyle \int (6x + 2)\left(3x^2 + 2x - 7\right)^5 dx$

3. $\displaystyle \int x^2 \left(x^3 + 10\right)^4 dx$

4. $\displaystyle \int \frac{\left(\sqrt{x} + 4\right)^3}{\sqrt{x}} dx$

5. $\displaystyle \int (24x + 8)\left(6x^2 + 4x - 5\right)^7 dx$

6. $\displaystyle \int \cos x \sin x \, dx$

7. $\displaystyle \int (10x - 3)\sqrt{5x^2 - 3x} \, dx$

8. $\displaystyle \int \frac{6x^2 + 4}{\sqrt[3]{4x^3 + 8x - 3}} dx$

9. $\displaystyle \int_0^1 \left(x^3 - 9x^2 + 2x\right)^3 \left(3x^2 - 18x + 2\right) dx$

10. $\displaystyle \int_{-1}^1 \frac{6x + 2}{\sqrt{9x^2 + 6x - 2}} dx$

Answer Key

1. $\displaystyle\int 2x\left(x^2-5\right)^6 dx = \frac{1}{7}\left(x^2-5\right)^7 + C$

2. $\displaystyle\int (6x+2)\left(3x^2+2x-7\right)^5 dx = \frac{1}{6}\left(3x^2+2x-7\right)^6 + C$

3. $\displaystyle\int x^2\left(x^3+10\right)^4 dx = \frac{1}{15}\left(x^3+10\right)^5 + C$

4. $\displaystyle\int \frac{\left(\sqrt{x}+4\right)^3}{\sqrt{x}} dx = \frac{1}{2}\left(\sqrt{x}+4\right)^4 + C$

5. $\displaystyle\int (24x+8)\left(6x^2+4x-5\right)^7 dx = \frac{1}{4}\left(6x^2+4x-5\right)^8 + C$

6. $\displaystyle\int \cos x \sin x\, dx = \frac{1}{2}\sin^2 x + C$

7. $\displaystyle\int (10x-3)\sqrt{5x^2-3x}\, dx = \frac{2}{3}\left(5x^2-3x\right)\sqrt{5x^2-3x} + C$

8. $\displaystyle\int \frac{6x^2+4}{\sqrt[3]{4x^3+8x-3}} dx = \frac{3}{4}\sqrt[3]{\left(4x^3+8x-3\right)^2} + C$

9. $\displaystyle\int_0^1 \left(x^3-9x^2+2x\right)^3\left(3x^2-18x+2\right) dx = 324$

10. $\displaystyle\int_{-1}^{1} \frac{6x+2}{\sqrt{9x^2+6x-2}} dx = \frac{2}{3}\sqrt{13} - \frac{2}{3}$

Solutions

1. $\displaystyle\int 2x\left(x^2-5\right)^6 dx$

   To rewrite the integral, let $u = x^2 - 5$:

   $$u = x^2 - 5$$

   $$\frac{du}{dx} = 2x$$

   $$\frac{du}{dx} \cdot dx = 2x\,dx$$

   $$du = 2x\,dx$$

   $$\int 2x\left(x^2-5\right)^6 dx = \int \underbrace{\left(x^2-5\right)^6}_{u^6}\,\underbrace{2x\,dx}_{du}$$

   The rewritten integral then becomes:

   $$\int u^6\,du$$

   Integrating:

   $$\int u^6\,du = \frac{1}{7}u^7 + C$$

   Reinserting the original expression for u:

   $$\int 2x\left(x^2-5\right)^6 dx = \frac{1}{7}\left(x^2-5\right)^7 + C$$

2. $\displaystyle\int \left(6x+2\right)\left(3x^2+2x-7\right)^5 dx$

   To rewrite the integral, let $u = 3x^2 + 2x - 7$:

   $$u = 3x^2 + 2x - 7$$

   $$\frac{du}{dx} = 6x + 2$$

   $$\frac{du}{dx} \cdot dx = \left(6x+2\right) dx$$

   $$du = \left(6x+2\right) dx$$

   $$\int \left(6x+2\right)\left(3x^2+2x-7\right)^5 dx = \int \underbrace{\left(3x^2+2x-7\right)^5}_{u^5}\,\underbrace{\left(6x+2\right) dx}_{du}$$

calculation cont. on next page...

Solution #2 from previous page...

The rewritten integral then becomes:

$$\int u^5 \, du$$

Integrating:

$$\int u^5 \, du = \frac{1}{6} u^6 + C$$

Reinserting the original expression for u:

$$\int (6x+2)(3x^2+2x-7)^5 \, dx = \frac{1}{6}(3x^2+2x-7)^6 + C$$

3. $$\int x^2 (x^3+10)^4 \, dx = \int (x^3+10)^4 \, x^2 dx$$

Letting $u = x^3 + 10$:

$$u = x^3 + 10$$

$$\frac{du}{dx} = 3x^2$$

$$\frac{du}{dx} \cdot dx = 3x^2 \, dx$$

$$du = 3x^2 \, dx$$

To make the substitution, we must insert a factor of 3 inside the integral, forcing us to also multiply by a factor of $\frac{1}{3}$ outside the integral to compensate:

$$\int (x^3+10)^4 \, x^2 dx = \frac{1}{3} \int \underbrace{(x^3+10)^4}_{u^4} \underbrace{3x^2 \, dx}_{du}$$

The rewritten integral then becomes:

$$\frac{1}{3} \int (x^3+10)^4 \, 3x^2 dx = \frac{1}{3} \int u^4 \, du$$

Integrating:

$$\frac{1}{3} \int u^4 \, du = \frac{1}{3}\left(\frac{1}{5} u^5 + C\right) = \frac{1}{15} u^5 + C$$

Reinserting the original expression for u:

$$\int x^2 (x^3+10)^4 \, dx = \frac{1}{15}(x^3+10)^5 + C$$

4. $\displaystyle\int \frac{\left(\sqrt{x}+4\right)^3}{\sqrt{x}}\,dx = \int \left(\sqrt{x}+4\right)^3 \cdot \frac{1}{\sqrt{x}}\,dx$

Letting $u = \sqrt{x}+4$:

$$u = \sqrt{x}+4$$

$$u = x^{\frac{1}{2}} + 4$$

$$\frac{du}{dx} = \frac{1}{2}x^{-\frac{1}{2}}$$

$$\frac{du}{dx} = \frac{1}{2\sqrt{x}}$$

$$\frac{du}{dx}\cdot dx = \frac{1}{2\sqrt{x}}\,dx$$

$$du = \frac{1}{2\sqrt{x}}\,dx$$

To rewrite the integral we must insert a factor of $\dfrac{1}{2}$ inside the integral, forcing us to also multiply by a factor of 2 outside the integral to compensate:

$$\int \left(\sqrt{x}+4\right)^3 \cdot \frac{1}{\sqrt{x}}\,dx = 2\int \underbrace{\left(\sqrt{x}+4\right)^3}_{u^3} \cdot \underbrace{\frac{1}{2\sqrt{x}}\,dx}_{du}$$

The rewritten integral then becomes:

$$2\int \left(\sqrt{x}+4\right)^3 \cdot \frac{1}{2\sqrt{x}}\,dx = 2\int u^3\,du$$

Integrating:

$$2\int u^3\,du = 2\left(\frac{1}{4}u^4 + C\right) = \frac{1}{2}u^4 + C$$

Reinserting the original expression for u:

$$\int \frac{\left(\sqrt{x}+4\right)^3}{\sqrt{x}}\,dx = \frac{1}{2}\left(\sqrt{x}+4\right)^4 + C$$

5. $\displaystyle\int(24x+8)\left(6x^2+4x-5\right)^7 dx = \int\left(6x^2+4x-5\right)^7(24x+8)\,dx$

Letting $u=6x^2+4x-5$:

$$u=6x^2+4x-5$$

$$\frac{du}{dx}=12x+4$$

$$\frac{du}{dx}\cdot dx=(12x+4)\,dx$$

$$du=(12x+4)\,dx$$

To make the substitution, we must insert a factor of $\dfrac{1}{2}$ inside the integral, forcing us to also multiply by a factor of 2 outside the integral to compensate:

$$\int\left(6x^2+4x-5\right)^7(24x+8)\,dx = 2\int\left(6x^2+4x-5\right)^7\frac{1}{2}(24x+8)\,dx$$

$$= 2\int\underbrace{\left(6x^2+4x-5\right)^7}_{u^7}\underbrace{(12x+4)\,dx}_{du}$$

Rewriting the integral:

$$2\int\left(6x^2+4x-5\right)^7(12x+4)\,dx = 2\int u^7\,du$$

Integrating:
$$2\int u^7\,du = 2\left(\frac{1}{8}u^8+C\right)=\frac{1}{4}u^8+C$$

Reinserting the original expression for u:

$$\int(24x+8)\left(6x^2+4x-5\right)^7 dx = \frac{1}{4}\left(6x^2+4x-5\right)^8+C$$

6. $\displaystyle\int\cos x\sin x\,dx$

Letting $u=\sin x$:

$$u=\sin x$$

$$\frac{du}{dx}=\cos x$$

$$\frac{du}{dx}\cdot dx=\cos x\,dx$$

$$du=\cos x\,dx$$

$$\Rightarrow \int\cos x\sin x\,dx = \int\underbrace{\sin x}_{u}\underbrace{\cos x\,dx}_{du}$$

calculation cont. on next page...

Solution #6 from previous page...

The rewritten integral then becomes:

$$\int \sin x \cos x \, dx = \int u \, du$$

Integrating:

$$\int u \, du = \frac{1}{2} u^2 + C$$

Reinserting the original expression for u:

$$\int \cos x \sin x \, dx = \frac{1}{2}(\sin x)^2 + C = \frac{1}{2} \sin^2 x + C$$

7. $$\int (10x-3)\sqrt{5x^2-3x} \, dx = \int (10x-3)(5x^2-3x)^{\frac{1}{2}} \, dx$$

$$= \int (5x^2-3x)^{\frac{1}{2}} (10x-3) \, dx$$

To rewrite the integral, let $u = 5x^2 - 3x$:

$$u = 5x^2 - 3x$$

$$\frac{du}{dx} = 10x - 3$$

$$\frac{du}{dx} \cdot dx = (10-3) \, dx$$

$$du = (10-3) \, dx$$

The rewritten integral then becomes:

$$\int \underbrace{(5x^2-3x)^{\frac{1}{2}}}_{u^{\frac{1}{2}}} \underbrace{(10x-3) \, dx}_{du} = \int u^{\frac{1}{2}} \, du$$

Integrating:

$$\int u^{\frac{1}{2}} \, du = \frac{2}{3} u^{\frac{3}{2}} + C = \frac{2}{3} u\sqrt{u} + C$$

Reinserting the original expression for u:

$$\int (10x-3)\sqrt{5x^2-3x} \, dx = \frac{2}{3}(5x^2-3x)\sqrt{5x^2-3x} + C$$

8. $$\int \frac{6x^2+4}{\sqrt[3]{4x^3+8x-3}}\,dx = \int \frac{6x^2+4}{\left(4x^3+8x-3\right)^{\frac{1}{3}}}\,dx$$

$$= \int \left(6x^2+4\right)\left(4x^3+8x-3\right)^{-\frac{1}{3}}\,dx$$

$$= \int \left(4x^3+8x-3\right)^{-\frac{1}{3}}\left(6x^2+4\right)\,dx$$

Letting $u = 4x^3+8x-3$:

$$u = 4x^3+8x-3$$

$$\frac{du}{dx} = 12x^2+8$$

$$\frac{du}{dx}\cdot dx = \left(12x^2+8\right)dx$$

$$du = \left(12x^2+8\right)dx$$

To make the substitution, we must insert a factor of 2 inside the integral, forcing us to also multiply by a factor of $\dfrac{1}{2}$ outside the integral to compensate:

$$\int \left(4x^3+8x-3\right)^{-\frac{1}{3}}\left(6x^2+4\right)dx = \frac{1}{2}\int \left(4x^3+8x-3\right)^{-\frac{1}{3}} 2\left(6x^2+4\right)dx$$

$$= \frac{1}{2}\int \underbrace{\left(4x^3+8x-3\right)^{-\frac{1}{3}}}_{u^{-\frac{1}{3}}}\underbrace{\left(12x^2+8\right)dx}_{du}$$

Rewriting the integral:

$$\frac{1}{2}\int \left(4x^3+8x-3\right)^{-\frac{1}{3}}\left(12x^2+8\right)dx = \frac{1}{2}\int u^{-\frac{1}{3}}\,du$$

Integrating: $$\frac{1}{2}\int u^{-\frac{1}{3}}\,du = \frac{1}{2}\left(\frac{3}{2}u^{\frac{2}{3}}+C\right) = \frac{3}{4}u^{\frac{2}{3}}+C = \frac{3}{4}\sqrt[3]{u^2}+C$$

Reinserting the original expression for u:

$$\int \frac{6x^2+4}{\sqrt[3]{4x^3+8x-3}}\,dx = \frac{3}{4}\sqrt[3]{\left(4x^3+8x-3\right)^2}+C$$

9. $\int\limits_{0}^{1} \left(x^3 - 9x^2 + 2x\right)^3 \left(3x^2 - 18x + 2\right) dx$

To solve this problem, we will use the method of substitution to integrate the function, ignoring the limits of integration until the end of the problem.

Letting $u = x^3 - 9x^2 + 2x$:

$$u = x^3 - 9x^2 + 2x$$

$$\frac{du}{dx} = 3x^2 - 18x + 2$$

$$\frac{du}{dx} \cdot dx = \left(3x^2 - 18x + 2\right) dx$$

$$du = \left(3x^2 - 18x + 2\right) dx$$

The rewritten integral then becomes:

$$\int \underbrace{\left(x^3 - 9x^2 + 2x\right)^3}_{u^3} \underbrace{\left(3x^2 - 18x + 2\right) dx}_{du} = \int u^3 \, du$$

Integrating:

$$\int u^3 \, du = \frac{1}{4} u^4 + C$$

Reinserting the original expression for u:

$$\int \left(x^3 - 9x^2 + 2x\right)^3 \left(3x^2 - 18x + 2\right) dx = \frac{1}{4}\left(x^3 - 9x^2 + 2x\right)^4 + C$$

Incorporating the limits of integration, we have:

$$\int\limits_{0}^{1} \left(x^3 - 9x^2 + 2x\right)^3 \left(3x^2 - 18x + 2\right) dx = \left[\frac{1}{4}\left(x^3 - 9x^2 + 2x\right)^4 + C\right]_{0}^{1}$$

$$= \left[\frac{1}{4}\left(1^3 - 9(1)^2 + 2(1)\right)^4 + C\right] - \left[\frac{1}{4}\left(0^3 - 9(0)^2 + 2(0)\right)^4 + C\right]$$

$$= \left[\frac{1}{4}(-6)^4 + C\right] - [0 + C]$$

$$= 324 + C - C$$

$$= 324$$

10. $\displaystyle\int_{-1}^{1} \frac{6x+2}{\sqrt{9x^2+6x-2}}\,dx = \int_{-1}^{1} \frac{6x+2}{\left(9x^2+6x-2\right)^{\frac{1}{2}}}\,dx$

$$= \int_{-1}^{1} \left(9x^2+6x-2\right)^{-\frac{1}{2}}\left(6x+2\right)dx$$

To solve this problem, we will use the method of substitution to integrate the function, ignoring the limits of integration until the end of the problem.

Letting $u = 9x^2+6x-2$:

$$u = 9x^2+6x-2$$

$$\frac{du}{dx} = 18x+6$$

$$\frac{du}{dx}\cdot dx = \left(18x+6\right)dx$$

$$du = \left(18x+6\right)dx$$

To make the substitution, we must insert a factor of 3 inside the integral, forcing us to also multiply by a factor of $\dfrac{1}{3}$ outside the integral to compensate:

$$\int\left(9x^2+6x-2\right)^{-\frac{1}{2}}\left(6x+2\right)dx = \frac{1}{3}\int\left(9x^2+6x-2\right)^{-\frac{1}{2}}3\left(6x+2\right)dx$$

$$= \frac{1}{3}\int\underbrace{\left(9x^2+6x-2\right)^{-\frac{1}{2}}}_{u^{-\frac{1}{2}}}\underbrace{\left(18x+6\right)dx}_{du}$$

The rewritten integral then becomes:

$$\frac{1}{3}\int\left(9x^2+6x-2\right)^{-\frac{1}{2}}\left(18x+6\right)dx = \frac{1}{3}\int u^{-\frac{1}{2}}\,du$$

Integrating: $\displaystyle\frac{1}{3}\int u^{-\frac{1}{2}}\,du = \frac{1}{3}\left(2u^{\frac{1}{2}}+C\right) = \frac{2}{3}u^{\frac{1}{2}}+C = \frac{2}{3}\sqrt{u}+C$

Reinserting the original expression for u:

$$\int\frac{6x+2}{\sqrt{9x^2+6x-2}}\,dx = \frac{2}{3}\sqrt{9x^2+6x-2}+C$$

calculation cont. on next page...

Solution #10 from previous page...

Incorporating the limits of integration, we have:

$$\int_{-1}^{1} \frac{6x+2}{\sqrt{9x^2+6x-2}}\, dx = \left[\frac{2}{3}\sqrt{9x^2+6x-2}+C\right]_{-1}^{1}$$

$$= \left[\frac{2}{3}\sqrt{9(1)^2+6(1)-2}+C\right]-\left[\frac{2}{3}\sqrt{9(-1)^2+6(-1)-2}+C\right]$$

$$= \left[\frac{2}{3}\sqrt{13}+C\right]-\left[\frac{2}{3}\sqrt{1}+C\right]$$

$$= \frac{2}{3}\sqrt{13}+C-\frac{2}{3}-C$$

$$= \frac{2}{3}\sqrt{13}-\frac{2}{3}$$

INTEGRATION
BY PARTS

Integrate each of the following using integration by parts.

1. $\int xe^x \, dx$

2. $\int xe^{2x} \, dx$

3. $\int x \sin x \, dx$

4. $\int x \cos x \, dx$

5. $\int x^2 e^x \, dx$

6. $\int_0^1 xe^{4x} \, dx$

7. $\int x \sin 6x \, dx$

8. $\int \text{Ln} \, 5x \, dx$

9. $\int x^2 \sin x \, dx$

10. $\int e^x \sin x \, dx$

Answer Key

1. $\displaystyle\int xe^x\,dx = xe^x - e^x + C$

2. $\displaystyle\int xe^{2x}\,dx = \frac{1}{2}xe^{2x} - \frac{1}{4}e^{2x} + C$

3. $\displaystyle\int x\sin x\,dx = -x\cos x + \sin x + C$

4. $\displaystyle\int x\cos x\,dx = x\sin x + \cos x + C$

5. $\displaystyle\int x^2 e^x\,dx = x^2 e^x - 2xe^x + 2e^x + C$

6. $\displaystyle\int_0^1 xe^{4x}\,dx = \frac{3}{16}e^4 + \frac{1}{16}$ or,

   $\displaystyle\int_0^1 xe^{4x}\,dx = 10.3$

7. $\displaystyle\int x\sin 6x\,dx = -\frac{1}{6}x\cos 6x + \frac{1}{36}\sin 6x + C$

8. $\displaystyle\int \text{Ln}\,5x\,dx = x\,\text{Ln}\,5x - x + C$

9. $\displaystyle\int x^2 \sin x\,dx = -x^2\cos x + 2x\sin x + 2\cos x + C$

10. $\displaystyle\int e^x \sin x\,dx = \frac{e^x \sin x - e^x \cos x}{2}$

Solutions

1. $\displaystyle\int xe^x\,dx$

   Choosing x to be u:

   $$\int \underset{\substack{\uparrow \quad \smile \\ u \quad dv}}{xe^x\,dx}$$

   $u = x$ $\qquad\qquad dv = e^x\,dx$

   $\dfrac{du}{dx} = 1$ $\qquad\qquad \dfrac{dv}{dx} = e^x$

   $du = dx$ $\qquad\qquad v = e^x$

   $$\int u\,dv = uv - \int v\,du$$

   $\Rightarrow \displaystyle\int xe^x\,dx = xe^x - \int e^x\,dx$

   $\displaystyle\int xe^x\,dx = xe^x - e^x + C$

2. $\displaystyle\int xe^{2x}\,dx$

   Choosing x to be u:

   $$\int \underset{\substack{\uparrow \quad \smile \\ u \quad dv}}{xe^{2x}\,dx}$$

   $u = x$ $\qquad\qquad dv = e^{2x}\,dx$

   $\dfrac{du}{dx} = 1$ $\qquad\qquad \dfrac{dv}{dx} = e^{2x}$

   $du = dx$ $\qquad\qquad v = \dfrac{1}{2}e^{2x}$

   $$\int u\,dv = uv - \int v\,du$$

   $\Rightarrow \displaystyle\int xe^{2x}\,dx = x\left(\dfrac{1}{2}e^{2x}\right) - \int \dfrac{1}{2}e^{2x}\,dx$

   $\displaystyle\int xe^{2x}\,dx = \dfrac{1}{2}xe^{2x} - \dfrac{1}{4}e^{2x} + C$

3. $\displaystyle\int x \sin x \, dx$

Choosing x to be u:

$$\int \underset{\underset{u}{\uparrow}}{x} \underset{dv}{\underbrace{\sin x \, dx}}$$

$u = x$ $\qquad\qquad$ $dv = \sin x \, dx$

$\dfrac{du}{dx} = 1$ $\qquad\qquad$ $\dfrac{dv}{dx} = \sin x$

$du = dx$ $\qquad\qquad$ $v = -\cos x$

$$\int u \, dv = uv - \int v \, du$$

$$\Rightarrow \int x \sin x \, dx = x(-\cos x) - \int -\cos x \, dx$$

$$\int x \sin x \, dx = -x \cos x + \int \cos x \, dx$$

$$\int x \sin x \, dx = -x \cos x + \sin x + C$$

4. $\displaystyle\int x \cos x \, dx$

Choosing x to be u:

$$\int \underset{\underset{u}{\uparrow}}{x} \underset{dv}{\underbrace{\cos x \, dx}}$$

$u = x$ $\qquad\qquad$ $dv = \cos x \, dx$

$\dfrac{du}{dx} = 1$ $\qquad\qquad$ $\dfrac{dv}{dx} = \cos x$

$du = dx$ $\qquad\qquad$ $v = \sin x$

$$\int u \, dv = uv - \int v \, du$$

$$\Rightarrow \int x \cos x \, dx = x \sin x - \int \sin x \, dx$$

$$\int x \cos x \, dx = x \sin x + \cos x + C$$

5. $\displaystyle\int x^2 e^x \, dx$

Because the x is squared in the integral, this problem requires us to use integration by parts twice.

First,

$$\int \underset{\substack{\uparrow \\ u}}{x^2} \underbrace{e^x \, dx}_{dv}$$

$u = x^2$ $\qquad\qquad dv = e^x \, dx$

$\dfrac{du}{dx} = 2x$ $\qquad\qquad \dfrac{dv}{dx} = e^x$

$du = 2x \, dx$ $\qquad\qquad v = e^x$

$$\int u \, dv = uv - \int v \, du$$

$\Rightarrow \displaystyle\int x^2 e^x \, dx = x^2 e^x - \int e^x \, (2x \, dx)$

$\displaystyle\int x^2 e^x \, dx = x^2 e^x - 2 \int x e^x \, dx$ ①

Next, to calculate the integral on the right side we must again integrate by parts.

$$\int x^2 e^x \, dx = x^2 e^x - 2 \int \underset{\substack{\uparrow \\ u}}{x} \underbrace{e^x \, dx}_{dv}$$

$u = x$ $\qquad\qquad dv = e^x \, dx$

$\dfrac{du}{dx} = 1$ $\qquad\qquad \dfrac{dv}{dx} = e^x$

$du = dx$ $\qquad\qquad v = e^x$

$$\int u \, dv = uv - \int v \, du$$

$\Rightarrow \displaystyle\int x e^x \, dx = x e^x - \int e^x \, dx$

$\displaystyle\int x e^x \, dx = x e^x - e^x$

Finally, substituting the result for the integral in Equation ①, we have our answer:

$$\int x^2 e^x \, dx = x^2 e^x - 2 \int x e^x \, dx$$

$$\int x^2 e^x \, dx = x^2 e^x - 2 \left[x e^x - e^x \right] + C$$

$$\int x^2 e^x \, dx = x^2 e^x - 2 x e^x + 2 e^x + C$$

6. $\displaystyle\int_0^1 xe^{4x}\,dx$

To solve a definite integral using integration by parts we integrate by parts ignoring the limits of integration until the end of the problem.

$$\int \underset{\substack{\uparrow \;\;\; \\ u \;\; dv}}{xe^{4x}\,dx}$$

$$u = x \qquad\qquad dv = e^{4x}\,dx$$

$$\frac{du}{dx} = 1 \qquad\qquad \frac{dv}{dx} = e^{4x}$$

$$du = dx \qquad\qquad v = \frac{1}{4}e^{4x}$$

$$\int u\,dv = uv - \int v\,du$$

$$\Rightarrow \int xe^{4x}\,dx = x\left(\frac{1}{4}e^{4x}\right) - \int \frac{1}{4}e^{4x}\,dx$$

$$\int xe^{4x}\,dx = \frac{1}{4}xe^{4x} - \frac{1}{16}e^{4x} + C$$

Having integrated the function, we now evaluate the result at the endpoints.

$$\int_0^1 xe^{4x}\,dx = \left[\frac{1}{4}xe^{4x} - \frac{1}{16}e^{4x} + C\right]_0^1$$

$$\int_0^1 xe^{4x}\,dx = \left[\frac{1}{4}(1)e^{4(1)} - \frac{1}{16}e^{4(1)} + C\right] - \left[\frac{1}{4}(0)e^{4(0)} - \frac{1}{16}e^{4(0)} + C\right]$$

$$\int_0^1 xe^{4x}\,dx = \frac{1}{4}e^4 - \frac{1}{16}e^4 + C + \frac{1}{16} - C$$

$$\int_0^1 xe^{4x}\,dx = \frac{3}{16}e^4 + \frac{1}{16}$$

Or, if we choose to express our answer as a decimal:

$$\int_0^1 xe^{4x}\,dx = 10.3$$

7. $\int x \sin 6x \, dx$

Choosing x to be u:

$\int \underset{\substack{\uparrow \\ u}}{x} \underset{dv}{\underbrace{\sin 6x \, dx}}$

$u = x$ $\qquad\qquad dv = \sin 6x \, dx$

$\dfrac{du}{dx} = 1$ $\qquad\qquad \dfrac{dv}{dx} = \sin 6x$

$du = dx$ $\qquad\qquad v = -\dfrac{1}{6} \cos 6x$

$\int u \, dv = uv - \int v \, du$

$\Rightarrow \int x \sin 6x \, dx = x\left(-\dfrac{1}{6}\cos 6x\right) - \int -\dfrac{1}{6}\cos 6x \, dx$

$\int x \sin 6x \, dx = -\dfrac{1}{6} x \cos 6x + \dfrac{1}{6}\int \cos 6x \, dx$

$\int x \sin 6x \, dx = -\dfrac{1}{6} x \cos 6x + \dfrac{1}{36} \sin 6x + C$

8. $\int \text{Ln } 5x \, dx$

Choosing $\text{Ln } 5x$ to be u:

$\int \underset{u}{\underbrace{\text{Ln } 5x}} \underset{dv}{\underbrace{dx}}$

$u = \text{Ln } 5x$ $\qquad\qquad dv = dx$

$\dfrac{du}{dx} = \dfrac{5}{5x}$ $\qquad\qquad \dfrac{dv}{dx} = 1$

$\dfrac{du}{dx} = \dfrac{1}{x}$ $\qquad\qquad v = x$

$du = \dfrac{1}{x} \cdot dx$

$\int u \, dv = uv - \int v \, du$

$\Rightarrow \int \text{Ln } 5x \, dx = \text{Ln } 5x (x) - \int x \cdot \dfrac{1}{x} \, dx$

$\int \text{Ln } 5x \, dx = x \, \text{Ln } 5x - \int dx$

$\int \text{Ln } 5x \, dx = x \, \text{Ln } 5x - x + C$

9. $\displaystyle\int x^2 \sin x\, dx$

Because the x is squared in the integral, we must use integration by parts twice to solve the problem.

First,

$$\int \underset{u}{\underbrace{x^2}}\ \underset{dv}{\underbrace{\sin x\, dx}}$$

$$u = x^2 \qquad\qquad dv = \sin x\, dx$$

$$\frac{du}{dx} = 2x \qquad\qquad \frac{dv}{dx} = \sin x$$

$$du = 2x\, dx \qquad\qquad v = -\cos x$$

$$\int u\, dv = uv - \int v\, du$$

$$\Rightarrow\ \int x^2 \sin x\, dx = x^2 \left(-\cos x\right) - \int -\cos x \left(2x\, dx\right)$$

$$\int x^2 \sin x\, dx = -x^2 \cos x + 2\int x \cos x\, dx \qquad\qquad \text{\textcircled{2}}$$

Next, we use integration by parts to solve the integral on the right side.

$$\int \underset{u}{\underbrace{x}}\ \underset{dv}{\underbrace{\cos x\, dx}}$$

$$u = x \qquad\qquad dv = \cos x\, dx$$

$$\frac{du}{dx} = 1 \qquad\qquad \frac{dv}{dx} = \cos x$$

$$du = dx \qquad\qquad v = \sin x$$

$$\int u\, dv = uv - \int v\, du$$

$$\Rightarrow\ \int x \cos x\, dx = x \sin x - \int \sin x\, dx$$

$$\int x \cos x\, dx = x \sin x + \cos x$$

Taking the result and substituting it into Equation \textcircled{2} we have:

$$\int x^2 \sin x\, dx = -x^2 \cos x + 2\int x \cos x\, dx$$

$$\int x^2 \sin x\, dx = -x^2 \cos x + 2\left[x \sin x + \cos x\right] + C$$

$$\int x^2 \sin x\, dx = -x^2 \cos x + 2x \sin x + 2\cos x + C$$

10. $\displaystyle\int e^x \sin x\, dx$

This problem requires multiple use of integration by parts as well as an interesting step of algebra to finish the problem. Since neither the exponential function nor the sine function will disappear if we take the derivative, we let u be the portion of the integral that will at least change if we take its derivative.

$$\int e^x \sin x\, dx = \int \underset{u}{\sin x}\, \underset{dv}{e^x\, dx}$$

$$u = \sin x \qquad\qquad dv = e^x\, dx$$

$$\frac{du}{dx} = \cos x \qquad\qquad \frac{dv}{dx} = e^x$$

$$du = \cos x\, dx \qquad\qquad v = e^x$$

$$\int u\, dv = uv - \int v\, du$$

$$\Rightarrow \int e^x \sin x\, dx = \sin x\left(e^x\right) - \int e^x \cos x\, dx$$

$$\int e^x \sin x\, dx = e^x \sin x - \int \cos x\left(e^x\, dx\right) \qquad ③$$

Again choosing the trigonometric function as u, we apply integration by parts to the integral on the right side of the equation.

$$\int e^x \sin x\, dx = e^x \sin x - \int \underset{u}{\cos x}\underset{dv}{\underbrace{\left(e^x\, dx\right)}}$$

$$u = \cos x \qquad\qquad dv = e^x\, dx$$

$$\frac{du}{dx} = -\sin x \qquad\qquad \frac{dv}{dx} = e^x$$

$$du = -\sin x\, dx \qquad\qquad v = e^x$$

$$\int u\, dv = uv - \int v\, du$$

$$\Rightarrow \int \cos x\left(e^x\, dx\right) = \cos x\left(e^x\right) - \int e^x \left(-\sin x\, dx\right)$$

$$\int \cos x\left(e^x\, dx\right) = e^x \cos x + \int e^x \sin x\, dx$$

Inserting our result into Equation ③ :

$$\int e^x \sin x\, dx = e^x \sin x - \left[e^x \cos x + \int e^x \sin x\, dx\right]$$

$$\int e^x \sin x\, dx = e^x \sin x - e^x \cos x - \int e^x \sin x\, dx$$

Realizing that the integrals on the left and right sides are the same, we add $\int e^x \sin x \, dx$ to both sides of the equation yielding:

$$2 \int e^x \sin x \, dx = e^x \sin x - e^x \cos x$$

Lastly, dividing both sides of the equation by 2 we have the solution to the original integral:

$$\frac{2 \int e^x \sin x \, dx}{2} = \frac{e^x \sin x - e^x \cos x}{2}$$

$$\int e^x \sin x \, dx = \frac{e^x \sin x - e^x \cos x}{2}$$

INTEGRATION
BY TABLES

25

Using the table of integrals found on the next two pages, integrate each of the following.

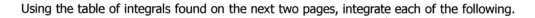

Notes

1. $\int \cot x \, dx$

2. $\int \mathrm{Ln}\, x \, dx$

3. $\int \cos^3 x \, dx$

4. $\int x^2 e^x \, dx$

5. $\int e^{4x} \sin 2x \, dx$

6. $\int \tan^{-1} x \, dx$

7. $\int \sin^{-1} x \, dx$

8. $\int x^6 \, \mathrm{Ln}\, x \, dx$

9. $\int \sin^4 x \, dx$

10. $\int \sqrt{x^2 + 16} \, dx$

11. $\int e^{2x} \cos 3x \, dx$

12. $\int \cos^5 x \, dx$

13. $\int \csc x \, dx$

14. $\int \sqrt{25 - x^2} \, dx$

15. $\int \dfrac{dx}{2x}$

16. $\displaystyle\int_{0}^{\frac{\pi}{2}} \sin^2 x \, dx$

17. $\displaystyle\int_{0}^{1} e^x \, dx$

18. $\displaystyle\int_{3}^{5} \sqrt{x^2 - 9} \, dx$

19. $\displaystyle\int_{0}^{\frac{\pi}{4}} \dfrac{2 \sin x}{\cos x} \, dx$

20. $\displaystyle\int_{0}^{\infty} e^{-2x^2} \, dx$

Table of Integrals

1 $\displaystyle\int u^n\,du = \frac{1}{n+1}u^{n+1} + C \quad\text{if } n \neq -1$

2 $\displaystyle\int \frac{du}{u} = \mathrm{Ln}|u| + C$

3 $\displaystyle\int \sin u\,du = -\cos u + C$

4 $\displaystyle\int \cos u\,du = \sin u + C$

5 $\displaystyle\int \tan u\,du = -\mathrm{Ln}|\cos u| + C$

6 $\displaystyle\int \cot u\,du = \mathrm{Ln}|\sin u| + C$

7 $\displaystyle\int \sec u\,du = \mathrm{Ln}|\sec u + \tan u| + C$

8 $\displaystyle\int \csc u\,du = \mathrm{Ln}|\csc u - \cot u| + C$

9 $\displaystyle\int \sin^2 u\,du = \frac{1}{2}u - \frac{1}{4}\sin 2u + C$

10 $\displaystyle\int \sin^3 u\,du = -\frac{1}{3}\left(2 + \sin^2 u\right)\cos u + C$

11 $\displaystyle\int \sin^n u\,du = -\frac{1}{n}\sin^{n-1} u \cos u + \frac{n-1}{n}\int \sin^{n-2} u\,du$

12 $\displaystyle\int \cos^2 u\,du = \frac{1}{2}u + \frac{1}{4}\sin 2u + C$

13 $\displaystyle\int \cos^3 u\,du = \frac{1}{3}\left(2 + \cos^2 u\right)\sin u + C$

14 $\displaystyle\int \cos^n u\,du = \frac{1}{n}\cos^{n-1} u \sin u + \frac{n-1}{n}\int \cos^{n-2} u\,du$

15 $\displaystyle\int e^u\,du = e^u + C$

16 $\displaystyle\int u e^u\,du = (u-1)e^u + C$

17 $\displaystyle\int u^n e^u\,du = u^n e^u - n\int u^{n-1} e^u\,du$

18 $\displaystyle\int \mathrm{Ln}\,u\,du = u\,\mathrm{Ln}\,u - u + C$

19 $\displaystyle\int u^n\,\mathrm{Ln}\,u\,du = \frac{u^{n+1}}{n+1}\mathrm{Ln}\,u - \frac{u^{n+1}}{(n+1)^2} + C$

20 $\displaystyle\int e^{au}\sin bu\,du = \frac{e^{au}}{a^2+b^2}\left(a\sin bu - b\cos bu\right) + C$

21 $\displaystyle\int e^{au} \cos bu \, du = \frac{e^{au}}{a^2 + b^2}(a\cos bu + b\sin bu) + C$

22 $\displaystyle\int \sin^{-1} u \, du = u\sin^{-1} u + \sqrt{1 - u^2} + C$

23 $\displaystyle\int \tan^{-1} u \, du = u\tan^{-1} u - \frac{1}{2}\operatorname{Ln}\left(1 + u^2\right) + C$

24 $\displaystyle\int \sec^{-1} u \, du = u\sec^{-1} u - \operatorname{Ln}\left|u + \sqrt{u^2 - 1}\right| + C$

25 $\displaystyle\int u\sin^{-1} u \, du = \frac{1}{4}\left(2u^2 - 1\right)\sin^{-1} u + \frac{u}{4}\sqrt{1 - u^2} + C$

26 $\displaystyle\int u\tan^{-1} u \, du = \frac{1}{2}\left(u^2 + 1\right)\tan^{-1} u - \frac{u}{2} + C$

27 $\displaystyle\int u\sec^{-1} u \, du = \frac{u^2}{2}\sec^{-1} u - \frac{1}{2}\sqrt{u^2 - 1} + C$

28 $\displaystyle\int \sqrt{u^2 \pm a^2} \, du = \frac{u}{2}\sqrt{u^2 \pm a^2} \pm \frac{a^2}{2}\operatorname{Ln}\left|u + \sqrt{u^2 \pm a^2}\right| + C$

29 $\displaystyle\int \sqrt{a^2 - u^2} \, du = \frac{u}{2}\sqrt{a^2 - u^2} + \frac{a^2}{2}\sin^{-1}\frac{u}{a} + C$

30 $\displaystyle\int_0^\infty e^{-au^2} \, du = \frac{1}{2}\sqrt{\frac{\pi}{a}} \quad \text{for } a > 0$

31 $\displaystyle\int \tan^2 u \, du = \tan u - u + C$

32 $\displaystyle\int \tan^3 u \, du = \frac{1}{2}\tan^2 u + \operatorname{Ln}\left|\cos u\right| + C$

33 $\displaystyle\int \sec^2 u \, du = \tan u + C$

34 $\displaystyle\int \sec^3 u \, du = \frac{1}{2}\sec u \tan u + \frac{1}{2}\operatorname{Ln}\left|\sec u + \tan u\right| + C$

35 $\displaystyle\int \csc^2 u \, du = -\cot u + C$

36 $\displaystyle\int \csc^3 u \, du = -\frac{1}{2}\csc u \cot u + \frac{1}{2}\operatorname{Ln}\left|\csc u - \cot u\right| + C$

37 $\displaystyle\int \cot^2 u \, du = -\cot u - u + C$

38 $\displaystyle\int \cot^3 u \, du = -\frac{1}{2}\cot^2 u - \operatorname{Ln}\left|\sin u\right| + C$

39 $\displaystyle\int \sinh u \, du = \cosh u + C$

40 $\displaystyle\int \cosh u \, du = \sinh u + C$

Answer Key

1. $\displaystyle\int \cot x\, dx = \text{Ln}\,|\sin x| + C$

2. $\displaystyle\int \text{Ln}\, x\, dx = x\,\text{Ln}\, x - x + C$

3. $\displaystyle\int \cos^3 x\, dx = \frac{1}{3}\left(2 + \cos^2 x\right)\sin x + C$

4. $\displaystyle\int x^2 e^x\, dx = x^2 e^x - 2(x-1)e^x + C$

5. $\displaystyle\int e^{4x} \sin 2x\, dx = \frac{e^{4x}}{20}\left(4\sin 2x - 2\cos 2x\right) + C$

6. $\displaystyle\int \tan^{-1} x\, dx = x\tan^{-1} x - \frac{1}{2}\,\text{Ln}\left(1 + x^2\right) + C$

7. $\displaystyle\int \sin^{-1} x\, dx = x\sin^{-1} + \sqrt{1 - x^2} + C$

8. $\displaystyle\int x^6\,\text{Ln}\, x\, dx = \frac{x^7}{7}\,\text{Ln}\, x - \frac{x^7}{49} + C$

9. $\displaystyle\int \sin^4 x\, dx = -\frac{1}{4}\sin^3 x\cos x + \frac{3}{8}x - \frac{3}{16}\sin 2x + C$

10. $\displaystyle\int \sqrt{x^2 + 16}\, dx = \frac{x}{2}\sqrt{x^2 + 16} + 8\,\text{Ln}\left|x + \sqrt{x^2 + 16}\right| + C$

11. $\displaystyle\int e^{2x}\cos 3x\, dx = \frac{e^{2x}}{13}\left(2\cos 3x + 3\sin 3x\right) + C$

12. $\displaystyle\int \cos^5 x\, dx = \frac{1}{5}\cos^4 x\sin x + \frac{4}{15}\left(2 + \cos^2 x\right)\sin x + C$

13. $\displaystyle\int \csc x\, dx = \text{Ln}\,|\csc x - \cot x| + C$

14. $\displaystyle\int \sqrt{25 - x^2}\, dx = \frac{x}{2}\sqrt{25 - x^2} + \frac{25}{2}\sin^{-1}\frac{x}{5} + C$

15. $\displaystyle\int \frac{dx}{2x} = \frac{1}{2}\,\text{Ln}\,|x| + C$

16. $\displaystyle\int_0^{\frac{\pi}{2}} \sin^2 x\, dx = \frac{\pi}{4}$

17. $\displaystyle\int_0^1 e^x\, dx = e - 1$

18. $\displaystyle\int_3^5 \sqrt{x^2 - 9}\, dx = 10 - \frac{9}{2}\,\text{Ln}\,|9| + \frac{9}{2}\,\text{Ln}\,|3|$

19. $\displaystyle\int_0^{\frac{\pi}{4}} \frac{2\sin x}{\cos x}\, dx = -2\,\text{Ln}\,\frac{\sqrt{2}}{2}$

20. $\displaystyle\int_0^{\infty} e^{-2x^2}\, dx = \frac{1}{2}\sqrt{\frac{\pi}{2}}$

Solutions

1. $\int \cot x \, dx$

   Using integral form #6 from the Table of Integrals:

   $$\int \cot x \, dx = \text{Ln}|\sin x| + C$$

2. $\int \text{Ln} \, x \, dx$

   Using integral form #18 from the Table of Integrals:

   $$\int \text{Ln} \, x \, dx = x \, \text{Ln} \, x - x + C$$

3. $\int \cos^3 x \, dx$

   Using integral form #13 from the Table of Integrals:

   $$\int \cos^3 x \, dx = \frac{1}{3}\left(2 + \cos^2 x\right)\sin x + C$$

4. $\int x^2 e^x \, dx$

   Realizing that $n = 2$ we first employ integral form #17 from the Table of Integrals to get:

   $$\int x^2 e^x \, dx = x^2 e^x - 2\int x^{2-1} e^x \, dx$$

   $$\int x^2 e^x \, dx = x^2 e^x - 2\int x e^x \, dx$$

   To finish, we apply integral form #16 to the remaining integral on the right side of the equation:

   $$\int x^2 e^x \, dx = x^2 e^x - 2\int x e^x \, dx$$

   $$\int x^2 e^x \, dx = x^2 e^x - 2\left[(x-1)e^x + C\right]$$

   $$\int x^2 e^x \, dx = x^2 e^x - 2(x-1)e^x + C$$

5. $\displaystyle\int e^{4x} \sin 2x \, dx$

Letting $a = 4$ and $b = 2$, we employ integral form #20 from the Table of Integrals:

$$\int e^{4x} \sin 2x \, dx = \frac{e^{4x}}{4^2 + 2^2} \left(4 \sin 2x - 2 \cos 2x\right) + C$$

$$\int e^{4x} \sin 2x \, dx = \frac{e^{4x}}{20} \left(4 \sin 2x - 2 \cos 2x\right) + C$$

6. $\displaystyle\int \tan^{-1} x \, dx$

Using integral form #23 from the Table of Integrals:

$$\int \tan^{-1} x \, dx = x \tan^{-1} x - \frac{1}{2} \text{Ln}\left(1 + x^2\right) + C$$

7. $\displaystyle\int \sin^{-1} x \, dx$

Using integral form #22 from the Table of Integrals:

$$\int \sin^{-1} x \, dx = x \sin^{-1} + \sqrt{1 - x^2} + C$$

8. $\displaystyle\int x^6 \, \text{Ln} \, x \, dx$

Letting $n = 6$ we employ integral form #19:

$$\int x^6 \, \text{Ln} \, x \, dx = \frac{x^{6+1}}{6+1} \text{Ln} \, x - \frac{x^{6+1}}{(6+1)^2} + C$$

$$\int x^6 \, \text{Ln} \, x \, dx = \frac{x^7}{7} \text{Ln} \, x - \frac{x^7}{49} + C$$

9. $\displaystyle\int \sin^4 x \, dx$

We begin by employing integral form #11 with $n = 4$:

$$\int \sin^4 x \, dx = -\frac{1}{4} \sin^{4-1} x \cos x + \frac{4-1}{4} \int \sin^{4-2} x \, dx$$

$$\int \sin^4 x \, dx = -\frac{1}{4} \sin^3 x \cos x + \frac{3}{4} \int \sin^2 x \, dx$$

To finish we apply integral form #9 to the integral on the right side of the equation.

$$\int \sin^4 x \, dx = -\frac{1}{4} \sin^3 x \cos x + \frac{3}{4} \left[\frac{1}{2} x - \frac{1}{4} \sin 2x + C\right]$$

$$\int \sin^4 x \, dx = -\frac{1}{4} \sin^3 x \cos x + \frac{3}{8} x - \frac{3}{16} \sin 2x + C$$

10. $\displaystyle\int \sqrt{x^2+16}\; dx$

Letting $u = x$ and $a = 4$, we employ integral form #28 from the Table of Integrals, remembering to use the top sign (+) in the integral form:

$$\int \sqrt{x^2+16}\; dx = \frac{x}{2}\sqrt{x^2+4^2} + \frac{4^2}{2}\,\mathrm{Ln}\left|x+\sqrt{x^2+4^2}\right| + C$$

$$\int \sqrt{x^2+16}\; dx = \frac{x}{2}\sqrt{x^2+16} + 8\,\mathrm{Ln}\left|x+\sqrt{x^2+16}\right| + C$$

11. $\displaystyle\int e^{2x}\cos 3x\; dx$

Letting $a = 2$ and $b = 3$, we employ integral form #21 from the Table of Integrals:

$$\int e^{2x}\cos 3x\; dx = \frac{e^{2x}}{2^2+3^2}\left(2\cos 3x + 3\sin 3x\right) + C$$

$$\int e^{2x}\cos 3x\; dx = \frac{e^{2x}}{13}\left(2\cos 3x + 3\sin 3x\right) + C$$

12. $\displaystyle\int \cos^5 x\; dx$

Letting $a = 5$, we employ integral form #14 from the Table of Integrals:

$$\int \cos^5 x\; dx = \frac{1}{5}\cos^{5-1} x \sin x + \frac{5-1}{5}\int \cos^{5-2} x\; dx$$

$$\int \cos^5 x\; dx = \frac{1}{5}\cos^4 x \sin x + \frac{4}{5}\int \cos^3 x\; dx$$

To finish, we apply integral form #13 to the integral on the right side of the equation:

$$\int \cos^5 x\; dx = \frac{1}{5}\cos^4 x \sin x + \frac{4}{5}\left[\frac{1}{3}\left(2+\cos^2 x\right)\sin x + C\right]$$

$$\int \cos^5 x\; dx = \frac{1}{5}\cos^4 x \sin x + \frac{4}{15}\left(2+\cos^2 x\right)\sin x + C$$

13. $\displaystyle\int \csc x\; dx$

Using integral form #8 from the Table of Integrals:

$$\int \csc x\; dx = \mathrm{Ln}\left|\csc x - \cot x\right| + C$$

14. $\int \sqrt{25-x^2}\,dx$

Letting $a=5$ and $u=x$, we employ integral form #29 from the Table of Integrals:

$$\int \sqrt{25-x^2}\,dx = \frac{x}{2}\sqrt{5^2-x^2} + \frac{5^2}{2}\sin^{-1}\frac{x}{5} + C$$

$$\int \sqrt{25-x^2}\,dx = \frac{x}{2}\sqrt{25-x^2} + \frac{25}{2}\sin^{-1}\frac{x}{5} + C$$

15. $\int \frac{dx}{2x} = \frac{1}{2}\int \frac{dx}{x}$

Using integral form #2 from the Table of Integrals:

$$\frac{1}{2}\int \frac{dx}{x} = \frac{1}{2}\Big[\mathrm{Ln}\,|x| + C\Big] = \frac{1}{2}\,\mathrm{Ln}\,|x| + C$$

$$\Rightarrow \quad \int \frac{dx}{2x} = \frac{1}{2}\,\mathrm{Ln}\,|x| + C$$

16. $\int_0^{\frac{\pi}{2}} \sin^2 x\,dx$

Using integral form #9 from the Table of Integrals:

$$\int_0^{\frac{\pi}{2}} \sin^2 x\,dx = \left[\frac{1}{2}x - \frac{1}{4}\sin 2x + C\right]_0^{\frac{\pi}{2}}$$

$$\int_0^{\frac{\pi}{2}} \sin^2 x\,dx = \left[\frac{1}{2}\left(\frac{\pi}{2}\right) - \frac{1}{4}\sin 2\left(\frac{\pi}{2}\right) + C\right] - \left[\frac{1}{2}(0) - \frac{1}{4}\sin 2(0) + C\right]$$

$$\int_0^{\frac{\pi}{2}} \sin^2 x\,dx = \left(\frac{\pi}{4} - \frac{1}{4}\sin \pi + C\right) - \left(0 - \frac{1}{4}\sin 0 + C\right)$$

$$\int_0^{\frac{\pi}{2}} \sin^2 x\,dx = \left(\frac{\pi}{4} - \frac{1}{4}(0) + C\right) - \left(-\frac{1}{4}(0) + C\right)$$

$$\int_0^{\frac{\pi}{2}} \sin^2 x\,dx = \frac{\pi}{4} + C - C$$

$$\int_0^{\frac{\pi}{2}} \sin^2 x\,dx = \frac{\pi}{4}$$

17. $\displaystyle\int_0^1 e^x\,dx$

Using integral form #15 from the Table of Integrals:

$$\int_0^1 e^x\,dx = \left[e^x + C\right]_0^1$$

$$\int_0^1 e^x\,dx = \left(e^1 + C\right) - \left(e^0 + C\right)$$

$$\int_0^1 e^x\,dx = e + C - 1 - C$$

$$\int_0^1 e^x\,dx = e - 1$$

18. $\displaystyle\int_3^5 \sqrt{x^2 - 9}\,dx$

Letting $u = x$ and $a = 3$, we use integral form #28, remembering to use the bottom sign in the integral form:

$$\int_3^5 \sqrt{x^2 - 9}\,dx = \left[\frac{x}{2}\sqrt{x^2 - 3^2} - \frac{3^2}{2}\,\text{Ln}\left|x + \sqrt{x^2 - 3^2}\right| + C\right]_3^5$$

$$\int_3^5 \sqrt{x^2 - 9}\,dx = \left[\frac{x}{2}\sqrt{x^2 - 9} - \frac{9}{2}\,\text{Ln}\left|x + \sqrt{x^2 - 9}\right| + C\right]_3^5$$

$$\int_3^5 \sqrt{x^2 - 9}\,dx = \left[\frac{5}{2}\sqrt{5^2 - 9} - \frac{9}{2}\,\text{Ln}\left|5 + \sqrt{5^2 - 9}\right| + C\right] - \left[\frac{3}{2}\sqrt{3^2 - 9} - \frac{9}{2}\,\text{Ln}\left|3 + \sqrt{3^2 - 9}\right| + C\right]$$

$$\int_3^5 \sqrt{x^2 - 9}\,dx = \left[\frac{5}{2}\sqrt{16} - \frac{9}{2}\,\text{Ln}\left|5 + \sqrt{16}\right| + C\right] - \left[\frac{3}{2}\sqrt{0} - \frac{9}{2}\,\text{Ln}\left|3 + \sqrt{0}\right| + C\right]$$

$$\int_3^5 \sqrt{x^2 - 9}\,dx = \left[\frac{5}{2}(4) - \frac{9}{2}\,\text{Ln}\left|5 + 4\right| + C\right] - \left[0 - \frac{9}{2}\,\text{Ln}\left|3\right| + C\right]$$

$$\int_3^5 \sqrt{x^2 - 9}\,dx = \left[10 - \frac{9}{2}\,\text{Ln}\left|9\right| + C\right] - \left[-\frac{9}{2}\,\text{Ln}\left|3\right| + C\right]$$

$$\int_3^5 \sqrt{x^2 - 9}\,dx = 10 - \frac{9}{2}\,\text{Ln}\left|9\right| + C + \frac{9}{2}\,\text{Ln}\left|3\right| - C$$

$$\int_3^5 \sqrt{x^2 - 9}\,dx = 10 - \frac{9}{2}\,\text{Ln}\left|9\right| + \frac{9}{2}\,\text{Ln}\left|3\right|$$

19. $\displaystyle\int_{0}^{\frac{\pi}{4}} \frac{2\sin x}{\cos x}\,dx = 2\int_{0}^{\frac{\pi}{4}} \frac{\sin x}{\cos x}\,dx$

Since $\dfrac{\sin x}{\cos x} = \tan x$, our integral becomes:

$\displaystyle 2\int_{0}^{\frac{\pi}{4}} \frac{\sin x}{\cos x}\,dx = 2\int_{0}^{\frac{\pi}{4}} \tan x\,dx$

Using integral form #5 from the Table of Integrals:

$\displaystyle 2\int_{0}^{\frac{\pi}{4}} \tan x\,dx = 2\Big[-\mathrm{Ln}\,|\cos x| + C\Big]_{0}^{\frac{\pi}{4}}$

$\displaystyle 2\int_{0}^{\frac{\pi}{4}} \tan x\,dx = 2\left[-\mathrm{Ln}\left|\cos \frac{\pi}{4}\right| + C\right] - 2\Big[-\mathrm{Ln}\,|\cos 0| + C\Big]$

$\displaystyle 2\int_{0}^{\frac{\pi}{4}} \tan x\,dx = 2\left(-\mathrm{Ln}\,\frac{\sqrt{2}}{2} + C\right) - 2\left(-\mathrm{Ln}\,1 + C\right)$

Since $\mathrm{Ln}\,1 = 0$:

$\displaystyle 2\int_{0}^{\frac{\pi}{4}} \tan x\,dx = 2\left(-\mathrm{Ln}\,\frac{\sqrt{2}}{2} + C\right) - 2\left(0 + C\right)$

$\displaystyle 2\int_{0}^{\frac{\pi}{4}} \tan x\,dx = -2\,\mathrm{Ln}\,\frac{\sqrt{2}}{2} + C - C$

$\displaystyle 2\int_{0}^{\frac{\pi}{4}} \tan x\,dx = -2\,\mathrm{Ln}\,\frac{\sqrt{2}}{2}$

20. $\displaystyle\int_{0}^{\infty} e^{-2x^2}\,dx$

Letting $a = 2$, we use integral form #30 from the Table of Integrals:

$\displaystyle\int_{0}^{\infty} e^{-2x^2}\,dx = \frac{1}{2}\sqrt{\frac{\pi}{2}}$

TRIGONOMETRIC SUBSTITUTION

26

Integrate each of the following using trigonometric substitution.

1. $\displaystyle\int \frac{dx}{\sqrt{x^2+16}}$

2. $\displaystyle\int \frac{x^2\,dx}{\sqrt{4-9x^2}}$

3. $\displaystyle\int \frac{dx}{\sqrt{x^2-16}}$

4. $\displaystyle\int \frac{dx}{x\sqrt{x^2+9}}$

5. $\displaystyle\int \frac{dx}{x\sqrt{4-x^2}}$

6. $\displaystyle\int \frac{\sqrt{x^2-4}}{x}\,dx$

7. $\displaystyle\int \frac{\sqrt{25+x^2}}{x^3}\,dx$

8. $\displaystyle\int \frac{dx}{\left(16-x^2\right)\sqrt{16-x^2}}$

9. $\displaystyle\int \frac{dx}{9-x^2}$

10. $\displaystyle\int_{2}^{4} \frac{x\,dx}{\sqrt{9x^2-36}}$

Answer Key

1. $\displaystyle\int \frac{dx}{\sqrt{x^2+16}} = \mathrm{Ln}\left|\sqrt{x^2+16}+x\right| - \mathrm{Ln}\left|4\right| + C$

2. $\displaystyle\int \frac{x^2\,dx}{\sqrt{4-9x^2}} = \frac{4\arcsin\dfrac{3x}{2} - 3x\sqrt{4-9x^2}}{54} + C$

3. $\displaystyle\int \frac{dx}{\sqrt{x^2-16}} = \mathrm{Ln}\left|x+\sqrt{x^2-16}\right| - \mathrm{Ln}\left|4\right| + C$

4. $\displaystyle\int \frac{dx}{x\sqrt{x^2+9}} = \frac{1}{3}\,\mathrm{Ln}\left|\sqrt{x^2+9}-3\right| - \frac{1}{3}\,\mathrm{Ln}\left|x\right| + C$

5. $\displaystyle\int \frac{dx}{x\sqrt{4-x^2}} = \frac{1}{2}\,\mathrm{Ln}\left|2-\sqrt{4-x^2}\right| - \frac{1}{2}\,\mathrm{Ln}\left|x\right| + C$

6. $\displaystyle\int \frac{\sqrt{x^2-4}}{x}\,dx = \sqrt{x^2-4} - 2\arccos\frac{2}{x} + C$

7. $\displaystyle\int \frac{\sqrt{25+x^2}}{x^3}\,dx = -\frac{\sqrt{25+x^2}}{2x} + \frac{1}{10}\,\mathrm{Ln}\left|\sqrt{25+x^2}-5\right| - \frac{1}{10}\,\mathrm{Ln}\left|x\right| + C$

8. $\displaystyle\int \frac{dx}{\left(16-x^2\right)\sqrt{16-x^2}} = \frac{x}{16\sqrt{16-x^2}} + C$

9. $\displaystyle\int \frac{dx}{9-x^2} = \frac{1}{3}\,\mathrm{Ln}\left|3+x\right| - \frac{1}{3}\,\mathrm{Ln}\left|\sqrt{9-x^2}\right| + C$

10. $\displaystyle\int_{2}^{4} \frac{x\,dx}{\sqrt{9x^2-36}} = \frac{2\sqrt{3}}{3}$

Solutions

Trigonometric Substitution Forms

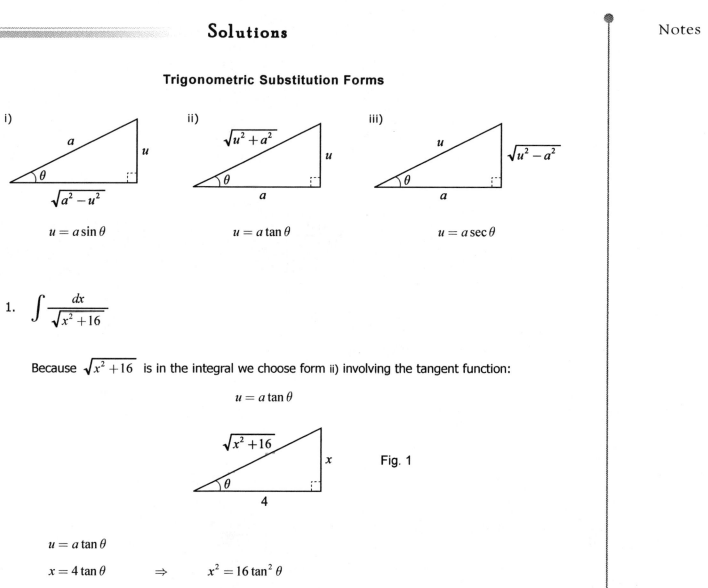

i)

$u = a\sin\theta$

ii)

$u = a\tan\theta$

iii)

$u = a\sec\theta$

1. $\displaystyle\int \frac{dx}{\sqrt{x^2+16}}$

Because $\sqrt{x^2+16}$ is in the integral we choose form ii) involving the tangent function:

$$u = a\tan\theta$$

Fig. 1

$u = a\tan\theta$

$x = 4\tan\theta \qquad \Rightarrow \qquad x^2 = 16\tan^2\theta$

$\dfrac{dx}{d\theta} = 4\sec^2\theta \qquad\qquad x^2+16 = 16\tan^2\theta + 16$

$dx = 4\sec^2\theta\,d\theta \qquad\qquad x^2+16 = 16\left(\tan^2\theta + 1\right)$

$\qquad\qquad\qquad\qquad x^2+16 = 16\sec^2\theta$

$\qquad\qquad\qquad\qquad \sqrt{x^2+16} = \sqrt{16\sec^2\theta}$

$\qquad\qquad\qquad\qquad \sqrt{x^2+16} = 4\sec\theta$

Substituting our results into the integral:

$$\int \frac{dx}{\sqrt{x^2+16}} = \int \frac{4\sec^2\theta\,d\theta}{4\sec\theta}$$

$$= \int \sec\theta\,d\theta$$

$$= \mathrm{Ln}\left|\sec\theta + \tan\theta\right| + C \qquad \text{(from the Table of Integrals on pg. #172)}$$

calculation cont. on next page...

Solution #1 from previous page...

From Fig. 1, $\sec\theta = \dfrac{\sqrt{x^2+16}}{4}$ and $\tan\theta = \dfrac{x}{4}$.

$$\Rightarrow \quad \int \frac{dx}{\sqrt{x^2+16}} = \operatorname{Ln}\left|\sec\theta + \tan\theta\right| + C$$

$$= \operatorname{Ln}\left| \frac{\sqrt{x^2+16}}{4} + \frac{x}{4} \right| + C$$

$$= \operatorname{Ln}\left| \frac{\sqrt{x^2+16}+x}{4} \right| + C$$

$$= \operatorname{Ln}\left| \sqrt{x^2+16}+x \right| - \operatorname{Ln}\left|4\right| + C$$

2. $\displaystyle\int \frac{x^2\,dx}{\sqrt{4-9x^2}}$

Because of the $\sqrt{4-9x^2}$ term, we use form i) involving the sine function:

$$u = a\sin\theta$$

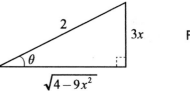

Fig. 2

$u = a\sin\theta$

$3x = 2\sin\theta$

$x = \dfrac{2}{3}\sin\theta \qquad \Rightarrow \qquad x^2 = \dfrac{4}{9}\sin^2\theta$

$\dfrac{dx}{d\theta} = \dfrac{2}{3}\cos\theta \qquad\qquad\quad 9x^2 = 4\sin^2\theta$

$\qquad\qquad\qquad\qquad\qquad 4-9x^2 = 4-4\sin^2\theta$

$dx = \dfrac{2}{3}\cos\theta\,d\theta \qquad\qquad 4-9x^2 = 4\left(1-\sin^2\theta\right)$

$\qquad\qquad\qquad\qquad\qquad 4-9x^2 = 4\cos^2\theta$

$\qquad\qquad\qquad\qquad\quad \sqrt{4-9x^2} = \sqrt{4\cos^2\theta}$

$\qquad\qquad\qquad\qquad\quad \sqrt{4-9x^2} = 2\cos\theta$

Solution #2 from previous page...

Substituting our results into the integral:

$$\int \frac{x^2 \, dx}{\sqrt{4-9x^2}} = \int \frac{\left(\dfrac{4}{9}\sin^2\theta\right)\left(\dfrac{2}{3}\cos\theta \, d\theta\right)}{2\cos\theta}$$

$$= \int \frac{4}{27}\sin^2\theta \, d\theta$$

$$= \frac{4}{27}\int \sin^2\theta \, d\theta$$

$$= \frac{4}{27}\left[\frac{1}{2}\theta - \frac{1}{4}\sin 2\theta + C\right] \qquad \text{(from the Table of Integrals on pg. #172)}$$

$$= \frac{4}{54}\theta - \frac{1}{27}\sin 2\theta + C$$

Using the trigonometric identity $\sin 2\theta = 2\sin\theta\cos\theta$, we are able to rewrite the 2nd term:

$$\int \frac{x^2 \, dx}{\sqrt{4-9x^2}} = \frac{4}{54}\theta - \frac{2}{27}\sin\theta\cos\theta + C$$

From Fig. 2,
$$\theta = \arcsin\frac{3x}{2}$$

$$\sin\theta = \frac{3x}{2}$$

$$\cos\theta = \frac{\sqrt{4-9x^2}}{2}$$

Thus,
$$\int \frac{x^2 \, dx}{\sqrt{4-9x^2}} = \frac{4}{54}\arcsin\frac{3x}{2} - \frac{2}{27}\left(\frac{3x}{2}\right)\left(\frac{\sqrt{4-9x^2}}{2}\right) + C$$

$$= \frac{4}{54}\arcsin\frac{3x}{2} - \frac{3x\sqrt{4-9x^2}}{54} + C$$

$$= \frac{4\arcsin\dfrac{3x}{2} - 3x\sqrt{4-9x^2}}{54} + C$$

3. $\displaystyle\int \frac{dx}{\sqrt{x^2-16}}$

Because of the $\sqrt{x^2-16}$ we use form iii) involving the secant function:

$$u = a\sec\theta$$

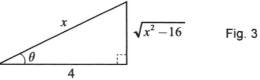

Fig. 3

$u = a\sec\theta$

$x = 4\sec\theta$ $\Rightarrow$ $x^2 = 16\sec^2\theta$

$\dfrac{dx}{d\theta} = 4\sec\theta\tan\theta$ $\qquad x^2-16 = 16\sec^2\theta-16$

$dx = 4\sec\theta\tan\theta\,d\theta$ $\qquad x^2-16 = 16\left(\sec^2\theta-1\right)$

$\qquad\qquad\qquad\qquad\qquad x^2-16 = 16\tan^2\theta$

$$\sqrt{x^2-16} = \sqrt{16\tan^2\theta}$$

$$\sqrt{x^2-16} = 4\tan\theta$$

Substituting our results into the integral:

$$\int \frac{dx}{\sqrt{x^2-16}} = \int \frac{4\sec\theta\tan\theta\,d\theta}{4\tan\theta}$$

$$= \int \sec\theta\,d\theta$$

$$= \mathrm{Ln}\left|\sec\theta+\tan\theta\right|+C \qquad \text{(from the Table of Integrals on pg. \#172)}$$

From Fig. 3,

$$\sec\theta = \frac{x}{4}$$

$$\tan\theta = \frac{\sqrt{x^2-16}}{4}$$

$\Rightarrow \displaystyle\int \frac{dx}{\sqrt{x^2-16}} = \mathrm{Ln}\left|\sec\theta+\tan\theta\right|+C$

$$= \mathrm{Ln}\left|\frac{x}{4}+\frac{\sqrt{x^2-16}}{4}\right|+C$$

$$= \mathrm{Ln}\left|\frac{x+\sqrt{x^2-16}}{4}\right|+C$$

$$= \mathrm{Ln}\left|x+\sqrt{x^2-16}\right|-\mathrm{Ln}\left|4\right|+C$$

4. $\displaystyle\int \frac{dx}{x\sqrt{x^2+9}}$

Because the integral contains $\sqrt{x^2+9}$, we will use form ii) involving the tangent function:

$$u = a\tan\theta$$

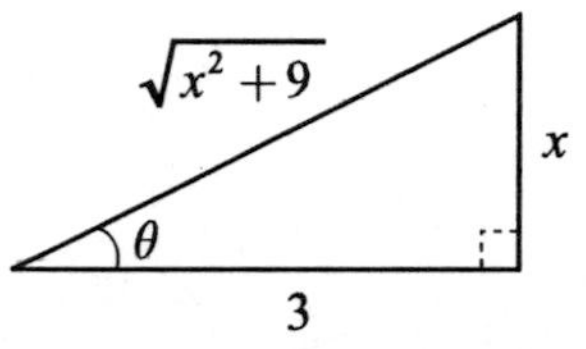

Fig. 4

$u = a\tan\theta$

$x = 3\tan\theta \qquad\Rightarrow\qquad x^2 = 9\tan^2\theta$

$\dfrac{dx}{d\theta} = 3\sec^2\theta \qquad\qquad x^2+9 = 9\tan^2\theta+9$

$dx = 3\sec^2\theta\, d\theta \qquad\qquad x^2+9 = 9\left(\tan^2\theta+1\right)$

$\qquad\qquad\qquad\qquad x^2+9 = 9\sec^2\theta$

$\qquad\qquad\qquad\qquad \sqrt{x^2+9} = \sqrt{9\sec^2\theta}$

$\qquad\qquad\qquad\qquad \sqrt{x^2+9} = 3\sec\theta$

Substituting the results into the integral:

$$\int \frac{dx}{x\sqrt{x^2+9}} = \int \frac{3\sec^2\theta\, d\theta}{\left(3\tan\theta\right)\left(3\sec\theta\right)}$$

$$= \int \frac{3\left(\dfrac{1}{\cos^2\theta}\right)d\theta}{3\left(\dfrac{\sin\theta}{\cos\theta}\right)(3)\left(\dfrac{1}{\cos\theta}\right)}$$

$$= \int \frac{d\theta}{3\sin\theta}$$

$$= \frac{1}{3}\int \frac{1}{\sin\theta}\cdot d\theta$$

$$= \frac{1}{3}\int \csc\theta\, d\theta$$

$$= \frac{1}{3}\,\mathrm{Ln}\left|\csc\theta-\cot\theta\right|+C \qquad \text{(from the Table of Integrals on pg. #172)}$$

calculation cont. on next page...

Solution #4 from previous page...

From Fig. 4,

$$\csc \theta = \frac{\sqrt{x^2 + 9}}{x}$$

$$\cot \theta = \frac{3}{x}$$

$$\Rightarrow \quad \int \frac{dx}{x\sqrt{x^2 + 9}} = \frac{1}{3} \mathrm{Ln} \left| \csc \theta - \cot \theta \right| + C$$

$$= \frac{1}{3} \mathrm{Ln} \left| \frac{\sqrt{x^2 + 9}}{x} - \frac{3}{x} \right| + C$$

$$= \frac{1}{3} \mathrm{Ln} \left| \frac{\sqrt{x^2 + 9} - 3}{x} \right| + C$$

$$= \frac{1}{3} \mathrm{Ln} \left| \sqrt{x^2 + 9} - 3 \right| - \frac{1}{3} \mathrm{Ln} \left| x \right| + C$$

5. $\displaystyle \int \frac{dx}{x\sqrt{4 - x^2}}$

Because of the $\sqrt{4 - x^2}$ term, we use form i) involving the sine function:

$$u = a \sin \theta$$

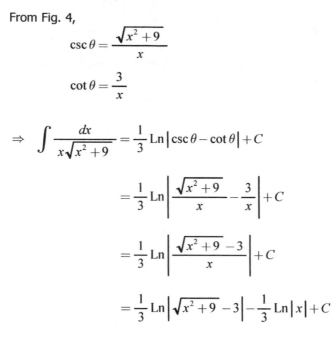

Fig. 5

$$u = a \sin \theta$$

$$x = 2 \sin \theta \qquad \Rightarrow \qquad x^2 = 4 \sin^2 \theta$$

$$\frac{dx}{d\theta} = 2 \cos \theta \qquad\qquad 4 - x^2 = 4 - 4 \sin^2 \theta$$

$$dx = 2 \cos \theta \, d\theta \qquad\qquad 4 - x^2 = 4 \left(1 - \sin^2 \theta \right)$$

$$4 - x^2 = 4 \cos^2 \theta$$

$$\sqrt{4 - x^2} = \sqrt{4 \cos^2 \theta}$$

$$\sqrt{4 - x^2} = 2 \cos \theta$$

calculation cont. on next page...

Solution #5 from previous page...

Substituting the results into the integral:

$$\int \frac{dx}{x\sqrt{4-x^2}} = \int \frac{2\cos\theta \, d\theta}{(2\sin\theta)(2\cos\theta)}$$

$$= \int \frac{d\theta}{2\sin\theta}$$

$$= \frac{1}{2}\int \csc\theta \, d\theta$$

$$= \frac{1}{2}\text{Ln}\left|\csc\theta - \cot\theta\right| + C$$

From Fig. 5,

$$\csc\theta = \frac{2}{x}$$

$$\cot\theta = \frac{\sqrt{4-x^2}}{x}$$

$$\Rightarrow \quad \int \frac{dx}{x\sqrt{4-x^2}} = \frac{1}{2}\text{Ln}\left|\frac{2}{x} - \frac{\sqrt{4-x^2}}{x}\right| + C$$

$$= \frac{1}{2}\text{Ln}\left|\frac{2-\sqrt{4-x^2}}{x}\right| + C$$

$$= \frac{1}{2}\text{Ln}\left|2-\sqrt{4-x^2}\right| - \frac{1}{2}\text{Ln}|x| + C$$

6. $$\int \frac{\sqrt{x^2-4}}{x}\,dx$$

Using form iii):

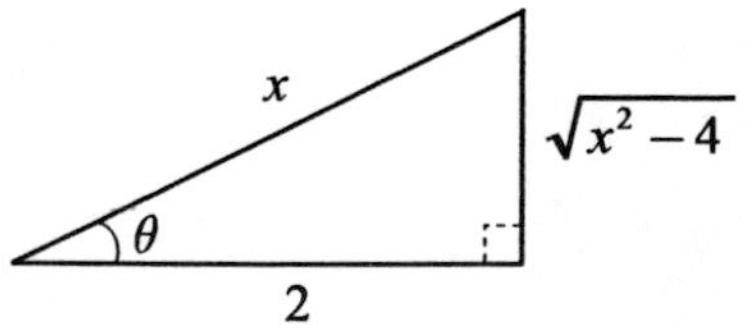

Fig. 6

$$u = a\sec\theta$$

$$x = 2\sec\theta \qquad \Rightarrow \qquad x^2 = 4\sec^2\theta$$

$$\frac{dx}{d\theta} = 2\sec\theta\tan\theta \qquad\qquad x^2 - 4 = 4\sec^2\theta - 4$$

$$dx = 2\sec\theta\tan\theta \, d\theta \qquad\qquad x^2 - 4 = 4\left(\sec^2\theta - 1\right)$$

$$x^2 - 4 = 4\tan^2\theta$$

$$\sqrt{x^2-4} = \sqrt{4\tan^2\theta}$$

$$\sqrt{x^2-4} = 2\tan\theta$$

calculation cont. on next page...

Solution #6 from previous page...

Substituting these results into the integral:

$$\int \frac{\sqrt{x^2-4}}{x}\,dx = \int \frac{2\tan\theta}{2\sec\theta}\left(2\sec\theta\tan\theta\,d\theta\right)$$

$$= \int 2\tan^2\theta\,d\theta$$

$$= 2\tan\theta - 2\theta + C \qquad\text{(from the Table of Integrals on pg. #172)}$$

From Fig. 6,

$$\tan\theta = \frac{\sqrt{x^2-4}}{2}$$

$$\theta = \arccos\frac{2}{x}$$

$$\Rightarrow \quad \int \frac{\sqrt{x^2-4}}{x}\,dx = 2\left(\frac{\sqrt{x^2-4}}{2}\right) - 2\arccos\frac{2}{x} + C$$

$$= \sqrt{x^2-4} - 2\arccos\frac{2}{x} + C$$

7. $\displaystyle\int \frac{\sqrt{25+x^2}}{x^3}\,dx$

Using form ii):

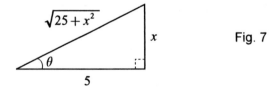

$$\sqrt{25+x^2}$$

x

Fig. 7

5

θ

$$u = a\tan\theta$$

$$x = 5\tan\theta \qquad\Rightarrow\qquad x^2 = 25\tan^2\theta$$

$$\frac{dx}{d\theta} = 5\sec^2\theta \qquad\qquad 25+x^2 = 25+25\tan^2\theta$$

$$\qquad\qquad 25+x^2 = 25\left(1+\tan^2\theta\right)$$

$$dx = 5\sec^2\theta\,d\theta \qquad\qquad 25+x^2 = 25\sec^2\theta$$

$$\sqrt{25+x^2} = \sqrt{25\sec^2\theta}$$

$$\sqrt{25+x^2} = 5\sec\theta$$

calculation cont. on next page...

Solution #7 from previous page...

Substituting our results into the integral:

$$\int \frac{\sqrt{25+x^2}}{x^3}\,dx = \int \frac{5\sec\theta}{125\tan^3\theta}\left(5\sec^2\theta\,d\theta\right)$$

$$= \int \frac{\sec^3\theta}{5\tan^3\theta}\,d\theta$$

$$= \frac{1}{5}\int \frac{\dfrac{1}{\cos^3\theta}}{\dfrac{\sin^3\theta}{\cos^3\theta}}\,d\theta$$

$$= \frac{1}{5}\int \frac{1}{\sin^3\theta}\,d\theta$$

$$= \frac{1}{5}\int \csc^3\,d\theta$$

$$= \frac{1}{5}\left[-\frac{1}{2}\csc\theta\cot\theta + \frac{1}{2}\mathrm{Ln}\left|\csc\theta-\cot\theta\right| + C\right] \qquad \text{(from the Table of Integrals on pg. #172)}$$

$$= -\frac{1}{10}\csc\theta\cot\theta + \frac{1}{10}\mathrm{Ln}\left|\csc\theta-\cot\theta\right| + C$$

From Fig. 7,

$$\csc\theta = \frac{\sqrt{25+x^2}}{x}$$

$$\cot\theta = \frac{5}{x}$$

$$\Rightarrow \quad \int \frac{\sqrt{25+x^2}}{x^3}\,dx = -\frac{1}{10}\left(\frac{\sqrt{25+x^2}}{x}\right)\left(\frac{5}{x}\right) + \frac{1}{10}\mathrm{Ln}\left|\frac{\sqrt{25+x^2}}{x} - \frac{5}{x}\right| + C$$

$$= -\frac{\sqrt{25+x^2}}{2x} + \frac{1}{10}\mathrm{Ln}\left|\frac{\sqrt{25+x^2}-5}{x}\right| + C$$

$$= -\frac{\sqrt{25+x^2}}{2x} + \frac{1}{10}\mathrm{Ln}\left|\sqrt{25+x^2}-5\right| - \frac{1}{10}\mathrm{Ln}\left|x\right| + C$$

8. $\displaystyle\int \frac{dx}{\left(16-x^2\right)\sqrt{16-x^2}}$

Because of the $\sqrt{16-x^2}$ we use form i) involving the sine function:

$$u = a\sin\theta$$

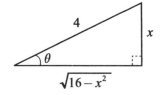

$$x$$

4

θ

$$\sqrt{16-x^2}$$

Fig. 8

$$u = a\sin\theta$$

$$x = 4\sin\theta \qquad \Rightarrow \qquad x^2 = 16\sin^2\theta$$

$$\frac{dx}{d\theta} = 4\cos\theta \qquad\qquad 16-x^2 = 16-16\sin^2\theta$$

$$dx = 4\cos\theta\, d\theta \qquad\qquad 16-x^2 = 16\left(1-\sin^2\theta\right)$$

$$16-x^2 = 16\cos^2\theta$$

$$\sqrt{16-x^2} = \sqrt{16\cos^2\theta}$$

$$\sqrt{16-x^2} = 4\cos\theta$$

Substituting our results into the integral:

$$\int \frac{dx}{\left(16-x^2\right)\sqrt{16-x^2}} = \int \frac{4\cos\theta\, d\theta}{\left(16\cos^2\theta\right)\left(4\cos\theta\right)}$$

$$= \int \frac{1}{16\cos^2\theta}\, d\theta$$

$$= \frac{1}{16}\int \sec^2\theta\, d\theta$$

$$= \frac{1}{16}\tan\theta + C$$

From Fig. 8,

$$\tan\theta = \frac{x}{\sqrt{16-x^2}}$$

$$\Rightarrow \int \frac{dx}{\left(16-x^2\right)\sqrt{16-x^2}} = \frac{1}{16}\cdot\frac{x}{\sqrt{16-x^2}} + C$$

$$= \frac{x}{16\sqrt{16-x^2}} + C$$

9. $\int \dfrac{dx}{9-x^2}$

Using form i):

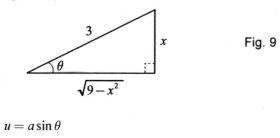

Fig. 9

$u = a\sin\theta$

$x = 3\sin\theta \qquad \Rightarrow \qquad x^2 = 9\sin^2\theta$

$\dfrac{dx}{d\theta} = 3\cos\theta \qquad\qquad 9 - x^2 = 9 - 9\sin^2\theta$

$dx = 3\cos\theta\,d\theta \qquad\qquad 9 - x^2 = 9\left(1 - \sin^2\theta\right)$

$\qquad\qquad\qquad\qquad\qquad 9 - x^2 = 9\cos^2\theta$

Substituting the results into the integral:

$$\int \frac{dx}{9-x^2} = \int \frac{3\cos\theta\,d\theta}{9\cos^2\theta}$$

$$= \int \frac{d\theta}{3\cos\theta}$$

$$= \frac{1}{3}\int \sec\theta\,d\theta$$

$$= \frac{1}{3}\,\mathrm{Ln}\left|\sec\theta + \tan\theta\right| + C \qquad \text{(from the Table of Integrals on pg. \#172)}$$

From Fig. 9,

$$\sec\theta = \frac{3}{\sqrt{9-x^2}}$$

$$\tan\theta = \frac{x}{\sqrt{9-x^2}}$$

$$\Rightarrow \int \frac{dx}{9-x^2} = \frac{1}{3}\,\mathrm{Ln}\left|\frac{3}{\sqrt{9-x^2}} + \frac{x}{\sqrt{9-x^2}}\right| + C$$

$$= \frac{1}{3}\,\mathrm{Ln}\left|\frac{3+x}{\sqrt{9-x^2}}\right| + C$$

$$= \frac{1}{3}\,\mathrm{Ln}\left|3+x\right| - \frac{1}{3}\,\mathrm{Ln}\left|\sqrt{9-x^2}\right| + C$$

10. $\displaystyle\int_{2}^{4} \frac{x\,dx}{\sqrt{9x^2-36}}$

Our strategy will be to integrate the functions using trigonometric substitution ignoring the limits of integration until the end of the problem.

Using form iii):

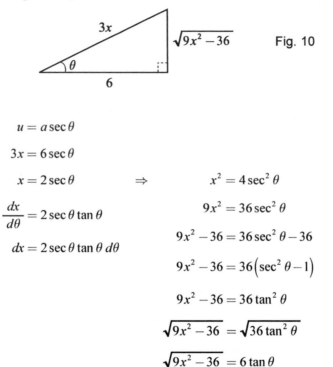

$$3x$$

$$\sqrt{9x^2-36}$$

Fig. 10

$$6$$

$$u = a\sec\theta$$

$$3x = 6\sec\theta$$

$$x = 2\sec\theta \qquad \Rightarrow \qquad x^2 = 4\sec^2\theta$$

$$\frac{dx}{d\theta} = 2\sec\theta\tan\theta \qquad\qquad 9x^2 = 36\sec^2\theta$$

$$dx = 2\sec\theta\tan\theta\,d\theta \qquad\qquad 9x^2 - 36 = 36\sec^2\theta - 36$$

$$9x^2 - 36 = 36\left(\sec^2\theta - 1\right)$$

$$9x^2 - 36 = 36\tan^2\theta$$

$$\sqrt{9x^2 - 36} = \sqrt{36\tan^2\theta}$$

$$\sqrt{9x^2 - 36} = 6\tan\theta$$

Substituting into the integral:

$$\int \frac{x\,dx}{\sqrt{9x^2-36}} = \int \frac{\left(2\sec\theta\right)\left(2\sec\theta\tan\theta\,d\theta\right)}{6\tan\theta}$$

$$= \int \frac{4}{6}\sec^2\theta\,d\theta$$

$$= \int \frac{2}{3}\sec^2\theta\,d\theta$$

$$= \frac{2}{3}\tan\theta + C$$

calculation cont. on next page...

Solution #10 from previous page...

From Fig. 10,
$$\tan \theta = \frac{\sqrt{9x^2 - 36}}{6}$$

$$\Rightarrow \int \frac{x\,dx}{\sqrt{9x^2 - 36}} = \frac{2}{3}\left(\frac{\sqrt{9x^2 - 36}}{6}\right) + C$$

$$= \frac{\sqrt{9x^2 - 36}}{9} + C$$

Incorporating the limits of integration:

$$\int_2^4 \frac{x\,dx}{\sqrt{9x^2 - 36}} = \left[\frac{\sqrt{9x^2 - 36}}{9} + C\right]_2^4$$

$$= \left[\frac{\sqrt{9(4)^2 - 36}}{9} + C\right] - \left[\frac{\sqrt{9(2)^2 - 36}}{9} + C\right]$$

$$= \left(\frac{\sqrt{144 - 36}}{9} + C\right) - \left(\frac{\sqrt{36 - 36}}{9} + C\right)$$

$$= \frac{\sqrt{108}}{9} + C - C$$

$$= \frac{\sqrt{108}}{9}$$

$$= \frac{2\sqrt{3}}{3}$$

NUMERICAL INTEGRATION

27

Approximate each of the following integrals using first Simpson's Rule:

$$\int_a^b f(x)\,dx \approx \frac{h}{3}\left[f(x_0)+4f(x_1)+2f(x_2)+\ldots+4f(x_{n-1})+f(x_n)\right]$$

and then the Trapezoidal Rule:

$$\int_a^b f(x)\,dx \approx \frac{h}{2}\left[f(x_0)+2f(x_1)+2f(x_2)+\ldots+2f(x_{n-1})+f(x_n)\right]$$

where $h = \dfrac{b-a}{n}$ for both rules.

1. $\displaystyle\int_1^3 x\,dx;$ $n = 8$

2. $\displaystyle\int_2^5 (x+1)\,dx;$ $n = 6$

3. $\displaystyle\int_0^2 x^2\,dx;$ $n = 8$

4. $\displaystyle\int_3^4 \sqrt{x}\,dx;$ $n = 10$

5. $\displaystyle\int_1^9 \frac{1}{x}\,dx;$ $n = 8$

Answer Key

1.

Simpson's Rule:

$$\int_1^3 x\,dx \approx 4.00$$

Trapezoidal Rule:

$$\int_1^3 x\,dx \approx 4.00$$

2.

Simpson's Rule:

$$\int_2^5 (x+1)\,dx \approx 13.5$$

Trapezoidal Rule:

$$\int_2^5 (x+1)\,dx \approx 13.5$$

3.

Simpson's Rule:

$$\int_0^2 x^2\,dx \approx 2.6667$$

Trapezoidal Rule:

$$\int_0^2 x^2\,dx \approx 2.6875$$

4.

Simpson's Rule:

$$\int_3^4 \sqrt{x}\,dx \approx 1.8693$$

Trapezoidal Rule:

$$\int_3^4 \sqrt{x}\,dx \approx 1.8692$$

5.

Simpson's Rule:

$$\int_1^9 \frac{1}{x}\,dx \approx 2.2101$$

Trapezoidal Rule:

$$\int_1^9 \frac{1}{x}\,dx \approx 2.2734$$

Solutions

1. $\displaystyle\int_1^3 x\,dx;$ $\qquad n=8$

Since $n=8$,
$$h=\frac{b-a}{n}.$$

$$h=\frac{3-1}{8}$$

$$h=\frac{2}{8}$$

$$h=0.25$$

$\Rightarrow$ $\quad x_0=1$ $\qquad f(x_0)=f(1)=1.00$

$\qquad x_1=1.25$ $\qquad f(x_1)=f(1.25)=1.25$

$\qquad x_2=1.50$ $\qquad f(x_2)=f(1.50)=1.50$

$\qquad x_3=1.75$ $\qquad f(x_3)=f(1.75)=1.75$

$\qquad x_4=2.00$ $\qquad f(x_4)=f(2.00)=2.00$

$\qquad x_5=2.25$ $\qquad f(x_5)=f(2.25)=2.25$

$\qquad x_6=2.50$ $\qquad f(x_6)=f(2.50)=2.50$

$\qquad x_7=2.75$ $\qquad f(x_7)=f(2.75)=2.75$

$\qquad x_8=3.00$ $\qquad f(x_8)=f(3.00)=3.00$

Simpson's Rule:

$$\int_1^3 x\,dx\approx\frac{0.25}{3}\Big[1.00+4(1.25)+2(1.50)+4(1.75)+2(2.00)+4(2.25)+2(2.50)+4(2.75)+3.00\Big]$$

$$\int_1^3 x\,dx\approx\frac{0.25}{3}\big(1.00+5.00+3.00+7.00+4.00+9.00+5.00+11.00+3.00\big)$$

$$\int_1^3 x\,dx\approx\frac{0.25}{3}\big(48.00\big)$$

$$\int_1^3 x\,dx\approx 4.00$$

calculation cont. on next page...

Solution #1 from previous page...

Trapezoidal Rule:

$$\int_{1}^{3} x\, dx \approx \frac{0.25}{2} \left[\begin{array}{l} 1.00 + 2(1.25) + 2(1.50) + 2(1.75) + 2(2.00) + 2(2.25) + 2(2.50) \\ + 2(2.75) + 3.00 \end{array} \right]$$

$$\int_{1}^{3} x\, dx \approx \frac{0.25}{2} \left(1.00 + 2.50 + 3.00 + 3.50 + 4.00 + 4.50 + 5.00 + 5.50 + 3.00 \right)$$

$$\int_{1}^{3} x\, dx \approx \frac{0.25}{2} (32.00)$$

$$\int_{1}^{3} x\, dx \approx 4.00$$

2. $\displaystyle\int_{2}^{5} (x+1)\, dx; \qquad n = 6$

Since $n = 6$,

$$h = \frac{b-a}{n}$$

$$h = \frac{5-2}{6}$$

$$h = \frac{3}{6}$$

$$h = 0.5$$

$\Rightarrow \quad x_0 = 2.0 \qquad\qquad f(x_0) = f(2.0) = 2.0 + 1 = 3.0$

$ x_1 = 2.5 \qquad\qquad f(x_1) = f(2.5) = 2.5 + 1 = 3.5$

$ x_2 = 3.0 \qquad\qquad f(x_2) = f(3.0) = 3.0 + 1 = 4.0$

$ x_3 = 3.5 \qquad\qquad f(x_3) = f(3.5) = 3.5 + 1 = 4.5$

$ x_4 = 4.0 \qquad\qquad f(x_4) = f(4.0) = 4.0 + 1 = 5.0$

$ x_5 = 4.5 \qquad\qquad f(x_5) = f(4.5) = 4.5 + 1 = 5.5$

$ x_6 = 5.0 \qquad\qquad f(x_6) = f(5.0) = 5.0 + 1 = 6.0$

calculation cont. on next page...

Solution #2 from previous page...

Simpson's Rule:

$$\int_{2}^{5} (x+1)\, dx \approx \frac{0.5}{3} \left[3.0 + 4(3.5) + 2(4.0) + 4(4.5) + 2(5.0) + 4(5.5) + 6.0 \right]$$

$$\int_{2}^{5} (x+1)\, dx \approx \frac{0.5}{3} \left(3.0 + 14.0 + 8.0 + 18.0 + 10.0 + 22.0 + 6.0 \right)$$

$$\int_{2}^{5} (x+1)\, dx \approx \frac{0.5}{3} (81.0)$$

$$\int_{2}^{5} (x+1)\, dx \approx 13.5$$

Trapezoidal Rule:

$$\int_{2}^{5} (x+1)\, dx \approx \frac{0.5}{2} \left[3.0 + 2(3.5) + 2(4.0) + 2(4.5) + 2(5.0) + 2(5.5) + 6.0 \right]$$

$$\int_{2}^{5} (x+1)\, dx \approx \frac{0.5}{2} \left(3.0 + 7.0 + 8.0 + 9.0 + 10.0 + 11.0 + 6.0 \right)$$

$$\int_{2}^{5} (x+1)\, dx \approx \frac{0.5}{2} (54)$$

$$\int_{2}^{5} (x+1)\, dx \approx 13.5$$

3. $\displaystyle\int_{0}^{2} x^2\, dx;$ $\qquad n = 8$

Since $n = 8$,

$$h = \frac{b-a}{n}$$

$$h = \frac{2-0}{8}$$

$$h = \frac{2}{8}$$

$$h = 0.25$$

calculation cont. on next page...

Solution #3 from previous page...

$\Rightarrow \quad x_0 = 0.00 \qquad\qquad f(x_0) = f(0.00) = (0.00)^2 = 0.0000$

$x_1 = 0.25 \qquad\qquad f(x_1) = f(0.25) = (0.25)^2 = 0.0625$

$x_2 = 0.50 \qquad\qquad f(x_2) = f(0.50) = (0.50)^2 = 0.2500$

$x_3 = 0.75 \qquad\qquad f(x_3) = f(0.75) = (0.75)^2 = 0.5625$

$x_4 = 1.00 \qquad\qquad f(x_4) = f(1.00) = (1.00)^2 = 1.0000$

$x_5 = 1.25 \qquad\qquad f(x_5) = f(1.25) = (1.25)^2 = 1.5625$

$x_6 = 1.50 \qquad\qquad f(x_6) = f(1.50) = (1.50)^2 = 2.2500$

$x_7 = 1.75 \qquad\qquad f(x_7) = f(1.75) = (1.75)^2 = 3.0625$

$x_8 = 2.00 \qquad\qquad f(x_8) = f(2.00) = (2.00)^2 = 4.0000$

Simpson's Rule:

$$\int_0^2 x^2\, dx \approx \frac{0.25}{3}\left[\begin{array}{l} 0.0000 + 4(0.0625) + 2(0.2500) + 4(0.5625) + 2(1.0000) + 4(1.5625) \\ +2(2.2500) + 4(3.0625) + 4.0000 \end{array}\right]$$

$$\int_0^2 x^2\, dx \approx \frac{0.25}{3}\left(\begin{array}{l} 0.0000 + 0.2500 + 0.5000 + 2.2500 + 2.0000 + 6.2500 + 4.5000 \\ +12.2500 + 4.0000 \end{array}\right)$$

$$\int_0^2 x^2\, dx \approx \frac{0.25}{3}(32.0000)$$

$$\int_0^2 x^2\, dx \approx 2.6667$$

Trapezoidal Rule:

$$\int_0^2 x^2\, dx \approx \frac{0.25}{2}\left[\begin{array}{l} 0.0000 + 2(0.0625) + 2(0.2500) + 2(0.5625) + 2(1.0000) + 2(1.5625) \\ +2(2.2500) + 2(3.0625) + 4.0000 \end{array}\right]$$

$$\int_0^2 x^2\, dx \approx \frac{0.25}{2}\left(\begin{array}{l} 0.0000 + 0.1250 + 0.5000 + 1.1250 + 2.0000 + 3.1250 + 4.5000 \\ +6.1250 + 4.0000 \end{array}\right)$$

$$\int_0^2 x^2\, dx \approx \frac{0.25}{2}(21.5000)$$

$$\int_0^2 x^2\, dx \approx 2.6875$$

4. $\displaystyle\int_{3}^{4} \sqrt{x}\, dx;$ $n = 10$

Since $n = 10$,

$$h = \frac{b-a}{n}$$

$$h = \frac{4-3}{10}$$

$$h = \frac{1}{10}$$

$$h = 0.1$$

$\Rightarrow$ $x_0 = 3.0$ $f(x_0) = f(3.0) = \sqrt{3.0} \approx 1.7321$

    $x_1 = 3.1$ $f(x_1) = f(3.1) = \sqrt{3.1} \approx 1.7607$

    $x_2 = 3.2$ $f(x_2) = f(3.2) = \sqrt{3.2} \approx 1.7889$

    $x_3 = 3.3$ $f(x_3) = f(3.3) = \sqrt{3.3} \approx 1.8166$

    $x_4 = 3.4$ $f(x_4) = f(3.4) = \sqrt{3.4} \approx 1.8439$

    $x_5 = 3.5$ $f(x_5) = f(3.5) = \sqrt{3.5} \approx 1.8708$

    $x_6 = 3.6$ $f(x_6) = f(3.6) = \sqrt{3.6} \approx 1.8974$

    $x_7 = 3.7$ $f(x_7) = f(3.7) = \sqrt{3.7} \approx 1.9235$

    $x_8 = 3.8$ $f(x_8) = f(3.8) = \sqrt{3.8} \approx 1.9494$

    $x_9 = 3.9$ $f(x_9) = f(3.9) = \sqrt{3.9} \approx 1.9748$

    $x_{10} = 4.0$ $f(x_{10}) = f(4.0) = \sqrt{4.0} = 2.0000$

Simpson's Rule:

$$\int_{3}^{4} \sqrt{x}\, dx \approx \frac{0.1}{3}\left[\begin{array}{l} 1.7321 + 4(1.7607) + 2(1.7889) + 4(1.8166) + 2(1.8439) + 4(1.8708) + 2(1.8974) \\ + 4(1.9235) + 2(1.9499) + 4(1.9748) + 2.0000 \end{array}\right]$$

$$\int_{3}^{4} \sqrt{x}\, dx \approx \frac{0.1}{3}\left(\begin{array}{l} 1.7321 + 7.0428 + 3.5778 + 7.2664 + 3.6878 + 7.4832 + 3.7948 + 7.6940 \\ + 3.8998 + 7.8992 + 2.0000 \end{array}\right)$$

$$\int_{3}^{4} \sqrt{x}\, dx \approx \frac{0.1}{3}(56.0779)$$

$$\int_{3}^{4} \sqrt{x}\, dx \approx 1.8693$$

calculation cont. on next page...

Solution #4 from previous page...

Trapezoidal Rule:

$$\int_3^4 \sqrt{x}\, dx \approx \frac{0.1}{2}\left[\begin{array}{l}1.7321+2(1.7607)+2(1.7889)+2(1.8166)+2(1.8439)+2(1.8708) \\ +2(1.8974)+2(1.9235)+2(1.9499)+2(1.9748)+2.0000\end{array}\right]$$

$$\int_3^4 \sqrt{x}\, dx \approx \frac{0.1}{2}\left(\begin{array}{l}1.7321+3.5214+3.5778+3.6332+3.6878+3.7416+3.7948 \\ +3.8470+3.8988+3.9496+2.0000\end{array}\right)$$

$$\int_3^4 \sqrt{x}\, dx \approx \frac{0.1}{2}(37.3841)$$

$$\int_3^4 \sqrt{x}\, dx \approx 1.8692$$

5. $\displaystyle\int_1^9 \frac{1}{x}\, dx; \qquad n=8$

Since $n=8$,

$$h=\frac{b-a}{n}$$

$$h=\frac{9-1}{8}$$

$$h=\frac{8}{8}$$

$$h=1$$

$$\Rightarrow \quad x_0=1 \qquad\qquad f(x_0)=f(1)=\frac{1}{1}=1.0000$$

$$x_1=2 \qquad\qquad f(x_1)=f(2)=\frac{1}{2}=0.5000$$

$$x_2=3 \qquad\qquad f(x_2)=f(3)=\frac{1}{3}\approx 0.3333$$

$$x_3=4 \qquad\qquad f(x_3)=f(4)=\frac{1}{4}=0.2500$$

$$x_4=5 \qquad\qquad f(x_4)=f(5)=\frac{1}{5}=0.2000$$

$$x_5=6 \qquad\qquad f(x_5)=f(6)=\frac{1}{6}\approx 0.1667$$

$$x_6=7 \qquad\qquad f(x_6)=f(7)=\frac{1}{7}\approx 0.1429$$

$$x_7=8 \qquad\qquad f(x_7)=f(8)=\frac{1}{8}=0.1250$$

$$x_8=9 \qquad\qquad f(x_8)=f(9)=\frac{1}{9}\approx 0.1111$$

calculation cont. on next page...

Solution #5 from previous page...

Simpson's Rule:

$$\int_1^9 \frac{1}{x}\, dx \approx \frac{1}{3}\left[\begin{array}{l}1.0000 + 4(0.5000) + 2(0.3333) + 4(0.2500) + 2(0.2000) + 4(0.1667) + 2(0.1429) \\ +4(0.1250) + 0.1111\end{array}\right]$$

$$\int_1^9 \frac{1}{x}\, dx \approx \frac{1}{3}\left[1.0000 + 2.0000 + 0.6666 + 1.0000 + 0.4000 + 0.6668 + 0.2858 + 0.5000 + 0.1111\right]$$

$$\int_1^9 \frac{1}{x}\, dx \approx \frac{1}{3}(6.6303)$$

$$\int_1^9 \frac{1}{x}\, dx \approx 2.2101$$

Trapezoidal Rule:

$$\int_1^9 \frac{1}{x}\, dx \approx \frac{1}{2}\left[\begin{array}{l}1.0000 + 2(0.5000) + 2(0.3333) + 2(0.2500) + 2(0.2000) + 2(0.1667) + 2(0.1429) \\ +2(0.1250) + 0.1111\end{array}\right]$$

$$\int_1^9 \frac{1}{x}\, dx \approx \frac{1}{2}(1.0000 + 1.0000 + 0.6666 + 0.5000 + 0.4000 + 0.3334 + 0.2858 + 0.2500 + 0.1111)$$

$$\int_1^9 \frac{1}{x}\, dx \approx \frac{1}{2}(4.5469)$$

$$\int_1^9 \frac{1}{x}\, dx \approx 2.2734$$

VOLUMES OF GEOMETRIC FIGURES

Find the volume of the figure generated by revolving each of the following functions between the given limits.

1. $f(x) = x;$ $x = 0$ and $x = 2$

2. $f(x) = x^2;$ $x = 0$ and $x = 1$

3. $f(x) = e^x;$ $x = 1$ and $x = 2$

4. $f(x) = \sqrt{x};$ $x = 0$ and $x = 4$

5. $f(x) = \dfrac{2}{x};$ $x = 1$ and $x = 5$

6. $f(x) = 2;$ $x = -3$ and $x = 2$

7. $f(x) = x - 1;$ $x = -1$ and $x = 3$

8. $f(x) = 2\sqrt{x};$ $x = 1$ and $x = 4$

9. $f(x) = x^3;$ $x = -2$ and $x = -1$

10. $f(x) = x^2 + x^3;$ $x = 0$ and $x = 1$

Answer Key

1. $V = \dfrac{8}{3}\pi \approx 8.38$

2. $V = \dfrac{1}{5}\pi \approx 0.63$

3. $V = \dfrac{\pi}{2}e^4 - \dfrac{\pi}{2}e^2 \approx 74.16$

4. $V = 8\pi \approx 25.13$

5. $V = \dfrac{16}{5}\pi \approx 10.05$

6. $V = 20\pi \approx 62.83$

7. $V = \dfrac{16}{3}\pi \approx 16.76$

8. $V = 30\pi \approx 94.25$

9. $V = \dfrac{127}{7}\pi \approx 57.00$

10. $V = \dfrac{71}{105}\pi \approx 2.12$

Solutions

1. $f(x) = x;$ $x = 0$ and $x = 2$

$$V = \int_0^2 \pi \left[f(x) \right]^2 dx$$

$$V = \int_0^2 \pi (x)^2 dx$$

$$V = \int_0^2 \pi x^2 dx$$

$$V = \left[\frac{1}{3} \pi x^3 \right]_0^2$$

$$V = \left[\frac{1}{3} \pi (2)^3 \right] - \left[\frac{1}{3} \pi (0)^3 \right]$$

$$V = \frac{8}{3} \pi - 0$$

$$V = \frac{8}{3} \pi \approx 8.38$$

2. $f(x) = x^2;$ $x = 0$ and $x = 1$

$$V = \int_0^1 \pi \left[f(x) \right]^2 dx$$

$$V = \int_0^1 \pi \left(x^2 \right)^2 dx$$

$$V = \int_0^1 \pi x^4 dx$$

$$V = \left[\frac{1}{5} \pi x^5 \right]_0^1$$

$$V = \left[\frac{1}{5} \pi (1)^5 \right] - \left[\frac{1}{5} \pi (0)^5 \right]$$

$$V = \frac{1}{5} \pi - 0$$

$$V = \frac{1}{5} \pi \approx 0.63$$

3. $f(x) = e^x; \qquad x = 1$ and $x = 2$

$$V = \int_1^2 \pi \left[f(x) \right]^2 dx$$

$$V = \int_1^2 \pi \left(e^x \right)^2 dx$$

$$V = \int_1^2 \pi e^{2x} dx$$

$$V = \left[\frac{\pi}{2} e^{2x} \right]_1^2$$

$$V = \left[\frac{\pi}{2} e^{2(2)} \right] - \left[\frac{\pi}{2} e^{2(1)} \right]$$

$$V = \frac{\pi}{2} e^4 - \frac{\pi}{2} e^2 \approx 74.16$$

4. $f(x) = \sqrt{x}; \qquad x = 0$ and $x = 4$

$$V = \int_0^4 \pi \left[f(x) \right]^2 dx$$

$$V = \int_0^4 \pi \left(\sqrt{x} \right)^2 dx$$

$$V = \int_0^4 \pi x \, dx$$

$$V = \left[\frac{1}{2} \pi x^2 \right]_0^4$$

$$V = \left[\frac{1}{2} \pi (4)^2 \right] - \left[\frac{1}{2} \pi (0)^2 \right]$$

$$V = 8\pi - 0$$

$$V = 8\pi \approx 25.13$$

5. $f(x) = \dfrac{2}{x}$; $x = 1$ and $x = 5$

$$V = \int_{1}^{5} \pi \left[f(x) \right]^2 dx$$

$$V = \int_{1}^{5} \pi \left(\frac{2}{x} \right)^2 dx$$

$$V = \int_{1}^{5} \pi \left(\frac{4}{x^2} \right) dx$$

$$V = \int_{1}^{5} \pi \left(4x^{-2} \right) dx$$

$$V = \left[\pi \left(-4x^{-1} \right) \right]_{1}^{5}$$

$$V = \left[-\frac{4\pi}{x} \right]_{1}^{5}$$

$$V = \left[-\frac{4\pi}{5} \right] - \left[-\frac{4\pi}{1} \right]$$

$$V = -\frac{4}{5}\pi + 4\pi$$

$$V = \frac{16}{5}\pi \approx 10.05$$

6. $f(x) = 2$; $x = -3$ and $x = 2$

$$V = \int_{-3}^{2} \pi \left[f(x) \right]^2 dx$$

$$V = \int_{-3}^{2} \pi (2)^2 dx$$

$$V = \int_{-3}^{2} 4\pi \, dx$$

$$V = \left[4\pi x \right]_{-3}^{2}$$

$$V = 4\pi (2) - 4\pi (-3)$$

$$V = 8\pi + 12\pi$$

$$V = 20\pi \approx 62.83$$

7. $f(x) = x - 1;$ $\qquad x = -1$ and $x = 3$

$$V = \int_{-1}^{3} \pi \left[f(x) \right]^2 dx$$

$$V = \int_{-1}^{3} \pi (x - 1)^2 dx$$

$$V = \int_{-1}^{3} \pi \left(x^2 - 2x + 1 \right) dx$$

$$V = \left[\pi \left(\frac{1}{3} x^3 - x^2 + x \right) \right]_{-1}^{3}$$

$$V = \left[\pi \left(\frac{1}{3} (3)^3 - (3)^2 + 3 \right) \right] - \left[\pi \left(\frac{1}{3} (-1)^3 - (-1)^2 + (-1) \right) \right]$$

$$V = \left[\pi (9 - 9 + 3) \right] - \left[\pi \left(-\frac{1}{3} - 1 - 1 \right) \right]$$

$$V = 3\pi + \frac{7}{3} \pi$$

$$V = \frac{16}{3} \pi \approx 16.76$$

8. $f(x) = 2\sqrt{x};$ $\qquad x = 1$ and $x = 4$

$$V = \int_{1}^{4} \pi \left[f(x) \right]^2 dx$$

$$V = \int_{1}^{4} \pi \left(2\sqrt{x} \right)^2 dx$$

$$V = \int_{1}^{4} \pi (4x) dx$$

$$V = \left[2\pi x^2 \right]_{1}^{4}$$

$$V = 2\pi (4)^2 - 2\pi (1)^2$$

$$V = 32\pi - 2\pi$$

$$V = 30\pi \approx 94.25$$

9. $f(x) = x^3;$ $x = -2$ and $x = -1$

$$V = \int_{-2}^{-1} \pi \left[f(x) \right]^2 dx$$

$$V = \int_{-2}^{-1} \pi \left(x^3 \right)^2 dx$$

$$V = \int_{-2}^{-1} \pi x^6 dx$$

$$V = \left[\frac{1}{7} \pi x^7 \right]_{-2}^{-1}$$

$$V = \frac{1}{7} \pi (-1)^7 - \frac{1}{7} \pi (-2)^7$$

$$V = -\frac{1}{7} \pi + \frac{128}{7} \pi$$

$$V = \frac{127}{7} \pi \approx 57.00$$

10. $f(x) = x^2 + x^3;$ $x = 0$ and $x = 1$

$$V = \int_{0}^{1} \pi \left[f(x) \right]^2 dx$$

$$V = \int_{0}^{1} \pi \left(x^2 + x^3 \right)^2 dx$$

$$V = \int_{0}^{1} \pi \left(x^4 + 2x^5 + x^6 \right) dx$$

$$V = \left[\pi \left(\frac{1}{5} x^5 + \frac{1}{3} x^6 + \frac{1}{7} x^7 \right) \right]_{0}^{1}$$

$$V = \left[\pi \left(\frac{1}{5} (1)^5 + \frac{1}{3} (1)^6 + \frac{1}{7} (1)^7 \right) \right] - \left[\pi \left(\frac{1}{5} (0)^5 + \frac{1}{3} (0)^6 + \frac{1}{7} (0)^7 \right) \right]$$

$$V = \pi \left(\frac{1}{5} + \frac{1}{3} + \frac{1}{7} \right) - 0$$

$$V = \frac{71}{105} \pi \approx 2.12$$

Evaluate each of the following.

1. $\displaystyle\int_{0}^{2}\int_{-1}^{1} 2x\,dxdy$

2. $\displaystyle\int_{0}^{1}\int_{-2}^{3} xy\,dxdy$

3. $\displaystyle\int_{-1}^{1}\int_{-2}^{1} (x+y)\,dydx$

4. $\displaystyle\int_{-2}^{0}\int_{1}^{2} \left(x+y^{2}\right)\,dydx$

5. $\displaystyle\int_{-1}^{2}\int_{0}^{1} e^{x+y}\,dxdy$

6. $\displaystyle\int_{-1}^{1}\int_{0}^{3}\int_{1}^{2} dxdydz$

7. $\displaystyle\int_{-2}^{0}\int_{0}^{3}\int_{-1}^{1} (x+y+z)\,dxdydz$

8. $\displaystyle\int_{-1}^{0}\int_{-1}^{1}\int_{0}^{1} e^{x+y+z}\,dydxdz$

9. $\displaystyle\int_{0}^{3}\int_{-2}^{2}\int_{0}^{1} (xy+yz+xz)\,dzdydx$

10. $\displaystyle\int_{1}^{4}\int_{0}^{2}\int_{-3}^{0} \left(x^{2}y+z^{3}-xyz\right)\,dxdydz$

Answer Key

1. $\displaystyle\int_{0}^{2}\int_{-1}^{1} 2x\, dxdy = 4$

2. $\displaystyle\int_{0}^{1}\int_{-2}^{3} xy\, dxdy = \frac{5}{4}$

3. $\displaystyle\int_{-1}^{1}\int_{-2}^{1} (x+y)\, dydx = -3$

4. $\displaystyle\int_{-2}^{0}\int_{1}^{2} \left(x+y^2\right) dydx = \frac{8}{3}$

5. $\displaystyle\int_{-1}^{2}\int_{0}^{1} e^{x+y}\, dxdy = e^3 - e^2 - 1 + \frac{1}{e}$

6. $\displaystyle\int_{-1}^{1}\int_{0}^{3}\int_{1}^{2} dxdydz = 6$

7. $\displaystyle\int_{-2}^{0}\int_{0}^{3}\int_{-1}^{1} (x+y+z)\, dxdydz = 6$

8. $\displaystyle\int_{-1}^{0}\int_{-1}^{1}\int_{0}^{1} e^{x+y+z}\, dydxdz = e^2 - 2e + \frac{2}{e} - \frac{1}{e^2}$

9. $\displaystyle\int_{0}^{3}\int_{-2}^{2}\int_{0}^{1} (xy+yz+xz)\, dzdydx = 9$

10. $\displaystyle\int_{1}^{4}\int_{0}^{2}\int_{-3}^{0} \left(x^2y+z^3-xyz\right) dxdydz = -261$

Solutions

1. $\displaystyle\int_0^2 \int_{-1}^1 2x\,dxdy$

First, we evaluate the inner integral involving dx:

$$\int_{-1}^1 2x\,dx = \left[x^2\right]_{-1}^1 = 1^2 - (-1)^2 = 1+1 = 2$$

$$\Rightarrow \int_0^2 \int_{-1}^1 2x\,dxdy = \int_0^2 2\,dy$$

Next, we evaluate the remaining integral:

$$\int_0^2 2\,dy = \left[2y\right]_0^2 = \left[2(2) - 2(0)\right] = 4$$

Thus,

$$\int_0^2 \int_{-1}^1 2x\,dxdy = 4$$

2. $\displaystyle\int_0^1 \int_{-2}^3 xy\,dxdy$

We begin by evaluating the inner integral involving dx, treating y as a constant:

$$\int_{-2}^3 xy\,dx = \left[\frac{x^2 y}{2}\right]_{-2}^3 = \left[\frac{3^2 \cdot y}{2} - \frac{(-2)^2 y}{2}\right]$$

$$= \frac{9y}{2} - \frac{4y}{2}$$

$$= \frac{5y}{2}$$

$$\Rightarrow \int_0^1 \int_{-2}^3 xy\,dxdy = \int_0^1 \frac{5y}{2}\,dy$$

calculation cont. on next page...

Solution #2 from previous page...

To finish the problem, we evaluate the remaining integral:

$$\int_0^1 \frac{5y}{2}\,dy = \left[\frac{5y^2}{4}\right]_0^1 = \left[\frac{5(1)^2}{4}\right] - \left[\frac{5(0)^2}{4}\right]$$

$$= \frac{5}{4} - 0$$

$$= \frac{5}{4}$$

Thus,

$$\int_0^1 \int_{-2}^3 xy\,dx\,dy = \frac{5}{4}$$

3. $\displaystyle\int_{-1}^1 \int_{-2}^1 (x+y)\,dy\,dx$

We begin by evaluating the inner integral involving dy, treating x as a constant:

$$\int_{-2}^1 (x+y)\,dy = \left[xy + \frac{y^2}{2}\right]_{-2}^1 = \left[x(1) + \frac{1^2}{2}\right] - \left[x(-2) + \frac{(-2)^2}{2}\right]$$

$$= \left(x + \frac{1}{2}\right) - (-2x + 2)$$

$$= x + \frac{1}{2} + 2x - 2$$

$$= 3x - \frac{3}{2}$$

$$\Rightarrow \quad \int_{-1}^1 \int_{-2}^1 (x+y)\,dy\,dx = \int_{-1}^1 \left(3x - \frac{3}{2}\right)dx$$

Evaluating the remaining integral:

$$\int_{-1}^1 \left(3x - \frac{3}{2}\right)dx = \left[\frac{3x^2}{2} - \frac{3}{2}x\right]_{-1}^1$$

$$= \left[\frac{3(1)^2}{2} - \frac{3}{2}(1)\right] - \left[\frac{3(-1)^2}{2} - \frac{3}{2}(-1)\right]$$

$$= \left(\frac{3}{2} - \frac{3}{2}\right) - \left(\frac{3}{2} + \frac{3}{2}\right)$$

$$= 0 - \frac{6}{2}$$

$$= -3$$

Thus,

$$\int_{-1}^1 \int_{-2}^1 (x+y)\,dy\,dx = -3$$

4. $\displaystyle\int_{-2}^{0}\int_{1}^{2}\left(x+y^2\right)dydx$

First, we evaluate the inner integral involving dy, treating x as a constant:

$$\int_{1}^{2}\left(x+y^2\right)dy = \left[xy+\frac{y^3}{3}\right]_{1}^{2} = \left[x(2)+\frac{2^3}{3}\right]-\left[x(1)+\frac{1^3}{3}\right]$$

$$= \left(2x+\frac{8}{3}\right)-\left(x+\frac{1}{3}\right)$$

$$= 2x+\frac{8}{3}-x-\frac{1}{3}$$

$$= x+\frac{7}{3}$$

$$\Rightarrow \int_{-2}^{0}\int_{1}^{2}\left(x+y^2\right)dydx = \int_{-2}^{0}\left(x+\frac{7}{3}\right)dx$$

Evaluating the remaining integral:

$$\int_{-2}^{0}\left(x+\frac{7}{3}\right)dx = \left[\frac{x^2}{2}+\frac{7}{3}x\right]_{-2}^{0} = \left[\frac{0^2}{2}+\frac{7}{3}(0)\right]-\left[\frac{(-2)^2}{2}+\frac{7}{3}(-2)\right]$$

$$= 0-\left(2-\frac{14}{3}\right)$$

$$= -\left(-\frac{8}{3}\right)$$

$$= \frac{8}{3}$$

Therefore,

$$\int_{-2}^{0}\int_{1}^{2}\left(x+y^2\right)dydx = \frac{8}{3}$$

5. $\displaystyle\int_{-1}^{2}\int_{0}^{1}e^{x+y}\,dxdy$

Evaluating the inner integral involving dx, treating y as a constant:

$$\int_{0}^{1}e^{x+y}\,dx = \left[e^{x+y}\right]_{0}^{1} = e^{1+y}-e^{0+y} = e^{1+y}-e^{y}$$

$$\Rightarrow \int_{-1}^{2}\int_{0}^{1}e^{x+y}\,dxdy = \int_{-1}^{2}\left(e^{1+y}-e^{y}\right)dy$$

calculation cont. on next page...

Solution #5 from previous page...

To finish the problem, we evaluate the remaining integral:

$$\int_{-1}^{2}\left(e^{1+y}-e^{y}\right)dy=\left[e^{1+y}-e^{y}\right]_{-1}^{2}=\left(e^{1+2}-e^{2}\right)-\left(e^{1+(-1)}-e^{-1}\right)$$

$$=\left(e^{3}-e^{2}\right)-\left(e^{0}-\frac{1}{e}\right)$$

$$=e^{3}-e^{2}-1+\frac{1}{e}$$

Thus,

$$\int_{-1}^{2}\int_{0}^{1}e^{x+y}\,dx\,dy=e^{3}-e^{2}-1+\frac{1}{e}$$

6. $$\int_{-1}^{1}\int_{0}^{3}\int_{1}^{2}dx\,dy\,dz$$

We begin by evaluating the innermost integral with respect to dx:

$$\int_{1}^{2}dx=\left[x\right]_{1}^{2}=2-1=1$$

$$\Rightarrow \int_{-1}^{1}\int_{0}^{3}\int_{1}^{2}dx\,dy\,dz=\int_{-1}^{1}\int_{0}^{3}1\cdot dy\,dz=\int_{-1}^{1}\int_{0}^{3}dy\,dz$$

Next, we evaluate the inner integral with respect to dy:

$$\int_{0}^{3}dy=\left[y\right]_{0}^{3}=3-0=3$$

$$\Rightarrow \int_{-1}^{1}\int_{0}^{3}\int_{1}^{2}dx\,dy\,dz=\int_{-1}^{1}3\,dz$$

Lastly, we evaluate the remaining integral with respect to dz:

$$\int_{-1}^{1}3\,dz=\left[3z\right]_{-1}^{1}=3(1)-3(-1)=3+3=6$$

Thus,

$$\int_{-1}^{1}\int_{0}^{3}\int_{1}^{2}dx\,dy\,dz=6$$

7. $\displaystyle\int_{-2}^{0}\int_{0}^{3}\int_{-1}^{1}(x+y+z)\,dx\,dy\,dz$

First, we evaluate the innermost integral involving dx, treating both y and z as constants:

$$\int_{-1}^{1}(x+y+z)\,dx = \left[\frac{x^2}{2}+yx+zx\right]_{-1}^{1}$$

$$= \left[\frac{1^2}{2}+y(1)+z(1)\right]-\left[\frac{(-1)^2}{2}+y(-1)+z(-1)\right]$$

$$= \left(\frac{1}{2}+y+z\right)-\left(\frac{1}{2}-y-z\right)$$

$$= \frac{1}{2}+y+z-\frac{1}{2}+y+z$$

$$= 2y+2z$$

$$\Rightarrow \int_{-2}^{0}\int_{0}^{3}\int_{-1}^{1}(x+y+z)\,dx\,dy\,dz = \int_{-2}^{0}\int_{0}^{3}(2y+2z)\,dy\,dz$$

Next, we evaluate the integral with respect to dy, treating z as a constant:

$$\int_{0}^{3}(2y+2z)\,dy = \left[y^2+2zy\right]_{0}^{3} = \left[3^2+2z(3)\right]-\left[0^2+2z(0)\right]$$

$$= 9+6z$$

$$\Rightarrow \int_{-2}^{0}\int_{0}^{3}\int_{-1}^{1}(x+y+z)\,dx\,dy\,dz = \int_{-2}^{0}(9+6z)\,dz$$

Calculating the remaining integral:

$$\int_{-2}^{0}(9+6z)\,dz = \left[9z+3z^2\right]_{-2}^{0} = \left[9(0)+3(0)^2\right]-\left[9(-2)+3(-2)^2\right]$$

$$= [0]-[-18+12]$$

$$= -(-6)$$

$$= 6$$

Thus,

$$\int_{-2}^{0}\int_{0}^{3}\int_{-1}^{1}(x+y+z)\,dx\,dy\,dz = 6$$

8. $\displaystyle\int_{-1}^{0}\int_{-1}^{1}\int_{0}^{1} e^{x+y+z}\,dy\,dx\,dz$

We begin by evaluating the innermost integral with respect to dy, holding both x and z constant:

$$\int_{0}^{1} e^{x+y+z}\,dy = \left[e^{x+y+z}\right]_{0}^{1} = e^{x+1+z} - e^{x+0+z} = e^{x+1+z} - e^{x+z}$$

$$\Rightarrow \int_{-1}^{0}\int_{-1}^{1}\int_{0}^{1} e^{x+y+z}\,dy\,dx\,dz = \int_{-1}^{0}\int_{-1}^{1}\left(e^{x+1+z} - e^{x+z}\right)dx\,dz$$

Next, we evaluate the integral with respect to dx, treating z as a constant:

$$\int_{-1}^{1}\left(e^{x+1+z} - e^{x+z}\right)dx = \left[e^{x+1+z} - e^{x+z}\right]_{-1}^{1}$$

$$= \left(e^{1+1+z} - e^{1+z}\right) - \left(e^{-1+1+z} - e^{-1+z}\right)$$

$$= e^{2+z} - e^{1+z} - e^{z} + e^{-1+z}$$

$$\Rightarrow \int_{-1}^{0}\int_{-1}^{1}\int_{0}^{1} e^{x+y+z}\,dy\,dx\,dz = \int_{-1}^{0}\left(e^{2+z} - e^{1+z} - e^{z} + e^{-1+z}\right)dz$$

Lastly, we evaluate the final integral with respect to dz:

$$\int_{-1}^{0}\left(e^{2+z} - e^{1+z} - e^{z} + e^{-1+z}\right)dz = \left[e^{2+z} - e^{1+z} - e^{z} + e^{-1+z}\right]_{-1}^{0}$$

$$= \left(e^{2+0} - e^{1+0} - e^{0} + e^{-1+0}\right) - \left(e^{2+(-1)} - e^{1+(-1)} - e^{-1} + e^{-1+(-1)}\right)$$

$$= \left(e^{2} - e^{1} - e^{0} + e^{-1}\right) - \left(e^{1} - e^{0} - e^{-1} + e^{-2}\right)$$

$$= \left(e^{2} - e - 1 + \frac{1}{e}\right) - \left(e - 1 - \frac{1}{e} + \frac{1}{e^{2}}\right)$$

$$= e^{2} - e - 1 + \frac{1}{e} - e + 1 + \frac{1}{e} - \frac{1}{e^{2}}$$

$$= e^{2} - 2e + \frac{2}{e} - \frac{1}{e^{2}}$$

Thus,

$$\int_{-1}^{0}\int_{-1}^{1}\int_{0}^{1} e^{x+y+z}\,dy\,dx\,dz = e^{2} - 2e + \frac{2}{e} - \frac{1}{e^{2}}$$

9. $\int\limits_{0}^{3}\int\limits_{-2}^{2}\int\limits_{0}^{1}(xy+yz+xz)\,dz\,dy\,dx$

We begin by evaluating the integral with respect to dz, treating both y and x as constants:

$$\int\limits_{0}^{1}(xy+yz+xz)\,dz = \left[xyz+\frac{yz^2}{2}+\frac{xz^2}{2}\right]_{0}^{1}$$

$$= \left[xy(1)+\frac{y(1)^2}{2}+\frac{x(1)^2}{2}\right]-\left[xy(0)+\frac{y(0)^2}{2}+\frac{x(0)^2}{2}\right]$$

$$= xy+\frac{y}{2}+\frac{x}{2}$$

$$\Rightarrow \int\limits_{0}^{3}\int\limits_{-2}^{2}\int\limits_{0}^{1}(xy+yz+xz)\,dz\,dy\,dx = \int\limits_{0}^{3}\int\limits_{-2}^{2}\left(xy+\frac{y}{2}+\frac{x}{2}\right)dy\,dx$$

Next, we evaluate the integral with respect to dy, treating x as a constant:

$$\int\limits_{-2}^{2}\left(xy+\frac{y}{2}+\frac{x}{2}\right)dy = \left[\frac{xy^2}{2}+\frac{y^2}{4}+\frac{xy}{2}\right]_{-2}^{2}$$

$$= \left[\frac{x(2)^2}{2}+\frac{2^2}{4}+\frac{x(2)}{2}\right]-\left[\frac{x(-2)^2}{2}+\frac{(-2)^2}{4}+\frac{x(-2)}{2}\right]$$

$$= (2x+1+x)-(2x+1-x)$$

$$= 2x+1+x-2x-1+x$$

$$= 2x$$

$$\Rightarrow \int\limits_{0}^{3}\int\limits_{-2}^{2}\int\limits_{0}^{1}(xy+yz+xz)\,dz\,dy\,dx = \int\limits_{0}^{3}2x\,dx$$

Lastly, we evaluate the remaining integral with respect to dx:

$$\int\limits_{0}^{3}2x\,dx = \left[x^2\right]_{0}^{3} = 3^2-0^2 = 9$$

Thus,

$$\int\limits_{0}^{3}\int\limits_{-2}^{2}\int\limits_{0}^{1}(xy+yz+xz)\,dz\,dy\,dx = 9$$

10. $\displaystyle\int_1^4\int_0^2\int_{-3}^0 \left(x^2y+z^3-xyz\right)dxdydz$

First, we evaluate the innermost integral with respect to dx, treating y and z as constants:

$$\int_{-3}^0 \left(x^2y+z^3-xyz\right)dx = \left[\frac{x^3y}{3}-xz^3-\frac{x^2yz}{2}\right]_{-3}^0$$

$$= \left[\frac{0^3y}{3}-(0)z^3-\frac{0^2yz}{2}\right] - \left[\frac{(-3)^3y}{3}-(-3)z^3-\frac{(-3)^2yz}{2}\right]$$

$$= [0] - \left[-9y+3z^3-\frac{9yz}{2}\right]$$

$$= 9y-3z^3+\frac{9yz}{2}$$

$$\Rightarrow \int_1^4\int_0^2\int_{-3}^0 \left(x^2y+z^3-xyz\right)dxdydz = \int_1^4\int_0^2\left(9y-3z^3+\frac{9yz}{2}\right)dydz$$

Next, we evaluate the inner integral with respect to dy, treating z as a constant:

$$\int_0^2\left(9y-3z^3+\frac{9yz}{2}\right)dy = \left[\frac{9y^2}{2}-3yz^3+\frac{9y^2z}{4}\right]_0^2$$

$$= \left[\frac{9(2)^2}{2}-3(2)z^3+\frac{9(2)^2z}{4}\right] - \left[\frac{9(0)^2}{2}-3(0)z^3+\frac{9(0)^2z}{4}\right]$$

$$= \left(18-6z^3+9z\right)-(0)$$

$$= 18-6z^3+9z$$

$$\Rightarrow \int_1^4\int_0^2\int_{-3}^0 \left(x^2y+z^3-xyz\right)dxdydz = \int_1^4\left(18-6z^3+9z\right)dz$$

calculation cont. on next page...

Solution #10 from previous page...

Lastly, we evaluate the remaining integral:

$$\int_1^4 \left(18 - 6z^3 + 9z\right) dz = \left[18z - \frac{3}{2}z^4 + \frac{9z^2}{2}\right]_1^4$$

$$= \left[18(4) - \frac{3}{2}(4)^4 + \frac{9(4)^2}{2}\right] - \left[18(1) - \frac{3}{2}(1)^4 + \frac{9(1)^2}{2}\right]$$

$$= (72 - 384 + 72) - \left(18 - \frac{3}{2} + \frac{9}{2}\right)$$

$$= (-240) - (21)$$

$$= -261$$

Thus,

$$\int_1^4 \int_0^2 \int_{-3}^0 \left(x^2 y + z^3 - xyz\right) dx\,dy\,dz = -261$$

DIFFERENTIAL
EQUATIONS

Show that each of the following is a solution to the given differential equation.

1. $\dfrac{d^2y}{dx^2} - \dfrac{dy}{dx} - 2y = 0;$ $\quad y = e^{2x}$

2. $\dfrac{x^2}{12} \cdot \dfrac{d^2y}{dx^2} - y = 0;$ $\quad y = x^4$

3. $\dfrac{d^2y}{dx^2} + y = 0;$ $\quad y = \cos x$

Find the general solution of each of the following differential equations.

4. $\dfrac{dy}{dx} = 2x$

5. $\dfrac{dy}{dx} = x^3$

6. $\dfrac{dy}{dx} = \dfrac{1}{x} + 3x$

7. $\dfrac{dy}{dx} = 2xy$

8. $\dfrac{dy}{dx} = x^2 y^2$

9. $y\dfrac{dy}{dx} + 2x = 0$

10. $\dfrac{dy}{dx} = \dfrac{y^2}{1+x}$

Find the particular solution of each of the following differential equations given each set of initial conditions.

11. $\dfrac{dy}{dx} = 3x^2;$ $\quad y = 1$ when $x = 0$

12. $\dfrac{dy}{dx} = e^{2x};$ $\quad y = -\dfrac{1}{2}$ when $x = 0$

13. $y\dfrac{dy}{dx} - 2x = 0;$ $\quad y = 4$ when $x = 0$

14. $x^2\dfrac{dy}{dx} + 3 = 0;$ $\quad y = \dfrac{1}{4}$ when $x = 6$

15. $\dfrac{dy}{dx} = 2e^x + \sqrt{x} + x^5;$ $\quad y = 7$ when $x = 0$

Answer Key

1. See Solutions

2. See Solutions

3. See Solutions

4. $y = x^2 + C$

5. $y = \dfrac{1}{4}x^4 + C$

6. $y = \operatorname{Ln} x + \dfrac{3}{2}x^2 + C$

7. $y = e^{x^2 + C}$

8. $y = -\dfrac{1}{\dfrac{1}{3}x^3 + C}$

9. $y = \sqrt{-2x^2 + C}$

10. $y = \dfrac{1}{-\operatorname{Ln}(1+x) + C}$

11. $y = x^3 + 1$

12. $y = \dfrac{1}{2}e^{2x} - 1$

13. $y = \sqrt{2x^2 + 16}$

14. $y = \dfrac{3}{x} - \dfrac{1}{4}$

15. $y = 2e^x + \dfrac{2}{3}x\sqrt{x} + \dfrac{1}{6}x^6 + 5$

Solutions

1. $\dfrac{d^2y}{dx^2} - \dfrac{dy}{dx} - 2y = 0;$ $y = e^{2x}$

   $y = e^{2x}$

   $\dfrac{dy}{dx} = 2e^{2x}$

   $\dfrac{d^2y}{dx^2} = 4e^{2x}$

   $\Rightarrow$ $\dfrac{d^2y}{dx^2} - \dfrac{dy}{dx} - 2y = 0$

   $4e^{2x} - 2e^{2x} - 2\left(e^{2x}\right) = 0$

   $4e^{2x} - 2e^{2x} - 2e^{2x} = 0$

   $0 = 0$ ✓

2. $\dfrac{x^2}{12} \cdot \dfrac{d^2y}{dx^2} - y = 0;$ $y = x^4$

   $y = x^4$

   $\dfrac{dy}{dx} = 4x^3$

   $\dfrac{d^2y}{dx^2} = 12x^2$

   $\Rightarrow$ $\dfrac{x^2}{12} \cdot \dfrac{d^2y}{dx^2} - y = 0$

   $\dfrac{x^2}{12}\left(12x^2\right) - x^4 = 0$

   $x^4 - x^4 = 0$

   $0 = 0$ ✓

3. $\dfrac{d^2 y}{dx^2} + y = 0;$ $y = \cos x$

$y = \cos x$

$\dfrac{dy}{dx} = -\sin x$

$\dfrac{d^2 y}{dx^2} = -\cos x$

$\Rightarrow$ $\dfrac{d^2 y}{dx^2} + y = 0$

$-\cos x + \cos x = 0$

$0 = 0$ ✓

4. $\dfrac{dy}{dx} = 2x$

$\dfrac{dy}{dx} \cdot dx = 2x \cdot dx$

$dy = 2x\, dx$

$\int dy = \int 2x\, dx$

$y = x^2 + C$

5. $\dfrac{dy}{dx} = x^3$

$\dfrac{dy}{dx} \cdot dx = x^3 \cdot dx$

$dy = x^3 dx$

$\int dy = \int x^3 dx$

$y = \dfrac{1}{4} x^4 + C$

6. $\dfrac{dy}{dx} = \dfrac{1}{x} + 3x$

$\dfrac{dy}{dx} \cdot dx = \left(\dfrac{1}{x} + 3x \right) dx$

$dy = \left(\dfrac{1}{x} + 3x \right) dx$

$\int dy = \int \left(\dfrac{1}{x} + 3x \right) dx$

$y = \operatorname{Ln} x + \dfrac{3}{2} x^2 + C$

7. $\dfrac{dy}{dx} = 2xy$

$\dfrac{dy}{dx} \cdot dx = 2xy \cdot dx$

$dy = 2xy \cdot dx$

$\dfrac{1}{y}\, dy = 2x\, dx$

$\int \dfrac{1}{y}\, dy = \int 2x\, dx$

$\operatorname{Ln} y = x^2 + C$

$e^{\operatorname{Ln} y} = e^{x^2 + C}$

$y = e^{x^2 + C}$

8. $\dfrac{dy}{dx} = x^2 y^2$

$\dfrac{dy}{dx} \cdot dx = x^2 y^2 \cdot dx$

$dy = x^2 y^2 dx$

$\dfrac{1}{y^2}\, dy = x^2 dx$

$\int \dfrac{1}{y^2}\, dy = \int x^2 dx$

$\int y^{-2} dy = \int x^2 dx$

$-y^{-1} = \dfrac{1}{3} x^3 + C$

$y^{-1} = -\dfrac{1}{3} x^3 + C$

$y = \dfrac{1}{-\dfrac{1}{3} x^3 + C}$

$y = -\dfrac{1}{\dfrac{1}{3} x^3 + C}$

9. $y\dfrac{dy}{dx}+2x=0$

$$y\dfrac{dy}{dx}=-2x$$

$$y\dfrac{dy}{dx}\cdot dx=-2x\cdot dx$$

$$y\,dy=-2x\,dx$$

$$\int y\,dy=\int-2x\,dx$$

$$\dfrac{1}{2}y^{2}=-x^{2}+C$$

$$y^{2}=-2x^{2}+C$$

$$y=\sqrt{-2x^{2}+C}$$

10. $\dfrac{dy}{dx}=\dfrac{y^{2}}{1+x}$

$$\dfrac{dy}{dx}\cdot dx=\dfrac{y^{2}}{1+x}\,dx$$

$$dy=\dfrac{y^{2}}{1+x}\,dx$$

$$\dfrac{1}{y^{2}}\,dy=\dfrac{1}{1+x}\,dx$$

$$\int\dfrac{1}{y^{2}}\,dy=\int\dfrac{1}{1+x}\,dx$$

$$\int y^{-2}\,dy=\int\dfrac{1}{1+x}\,dx$$

$$-y^{-1}=\operatorname{Ln}(1+x)+C$$

$$y^{-1}=-\operatorname{Ln}(1+x)+C$$

$$y=\dfrac{1}{-\operatorname{Ln}(1+x)+C}$$

11. $\dfrac{dy}{dx} = 3x^2;$ $\quad y = 1$ when $x = 0$

$$\frac{dy}{dx} \cdot dx = 3x^2 \cdot dx$$

$$dy = 3x^2 dx$$

$$\int dy = \int 3x^2 dx$$

$$y = x^3 + C$$

Inserting the initial conditions we find C:

$$y = x^3 + C$$

$$1 = (0)^3 + C$$

$$1 = C$$

The particular solution is therefore:

$$y = x^3 + 1$$

12. $\dfrac{dy}{dx} = e^{2x};$ $\quad y = -\dfrac{1}{2}$ when $x = 0$

$$\frac{dy}{dx} \cdot dx = e^{2x} \cdot dx$$

$$dy = e^{2x} dx$$

$$\int dy = \int e^{2x} dx$$

$$y = \frac{1}{2} e^{2x} + C$$

Inserting the initial conditions we find C:

$$y = \frac{1}{2} e^{2x} + C$$

$$-\frac{1}{2} = \frac{1}{2} e^{2(0)} + C$$

$$-\frac{1}{2} = \frac{1}{2}(1) + C$$

$$-1 = C$$

The particular solution is therefore:

$$y = \frac{1}{2} e^{2x} - 1$$

13. $y\dfrac{dy}{dx} - 2x = 0;$ $\qquad y = 4$ when $x = 0$

$$y\dfrac{dy}{dx} = 2x$$

$$y\dfrac{dy}{dx} \cdot dx = 2x \cdot dx$$

$$y\,dy = 2x\,dx$$

$$\int y\,dy = \int 2x\,dx$$

$$\dfrac{1}{2}y^2 = x^2 + C$$

$$y^2 = 2x^2 + C$$

$$y = \sqrt{2x^2 + C}$$

Inserting the initial conditions we find C:

$$4 = \sqrt{2(0)^2 + C}$$

$$4 = \sqrt{C}$$

$$16 = C$$

The particular solution is therefore:

$$y = \sqrt{2x^2 + 16}$$

14. $x^2 \dfrac{dy}{dx} + 3 = 0;$ $y = \dfrac{1}{4}$ when $x = 6$

$$x^2 \frac{dy}{dx} = -3$$

$$\frac{dy}{dx} = \frac{-3}{x^2}$$

$$\frac{dy}{dx} \cdot dx = \frac{-3}{x^2} \cdot dx$$

$$dy = \frac{-3}{x^2} dx$$

$$\int dy = \int \frac{-3}{x^2} dx$$

$$\int dy = \int -3x^{-2} dx$$

$$y = 3x^{-1} + C$$

$$y = \frac{3}{x} + C$$

Inserting the initial conditions we find C:

$$y = \frac{3}{x} + C$$

$$\frac{1}{4} = \frac{3}{6} + C$$

$$\frac{1}{4} = \frac{1}{2} + C$$

$$-\frac{1}{4} = C$$

The particular solution is therefore:

$$y = \frac{3}{x} - \frac{1}{4}$$

15. $\dfrac{dy}{dx} = 2e^x + \sqrt{x} + x^5;$ $\quad y = 7$ when $x = 0$

$$\frac{dy}{dx} = 2e^x + x^{\frac{1}{2}} + x^5$$

$$\frac{dy}{dx} \cdot dx = \left(2e^x + x^{\frac{1}{2}} + x^5\right) dx$$

$$dy = \left(2e^x + x^{\frac{1}{2}} + x^5\right) dx$$

$$\int dy = \int \left(2e^x + x^{\frac{1}{2}} + x^5\right) dx$$

$$y = 2e^x + \frac{2}{3} x^{\frac{3}{2}} + \frac{1}{6} x^6 + C$$

$$y = 2e^x + \frac{2}{3} x\sqrt{x} + \frac{1}{6} x^6 + C$$

Inserting the initial conditions we find C:

$$y = 2e^x + \frac{2}{3} x\sqrt{x} + \frac{1}{6} x^6 + C$$

$$7 = 2e^0 + \frac{2}{3}(0)\sqrt{0} + \frac{1}{6}(0)^6 + C$$

$$7 = 2(1) + 0 + 0 + C$$

$$7 = 2 + C$$

$$5 = C$$

The particular solution is therefore:

$$y = 2e^x + \frac{2}{3} x\sqrt{x} + \frac{1}{6} x^6 + 5$$

Final
Examination I

Find the derivative of each of the following:

1. $f(x) = x^2 + 6x - 5$

2. $y = (4 + 3x)(7x^2 - 8x + 2)$

3. $y = e^{9x^3}$

4. $f(x) = \sin x^3$

5. $f(x) = \tan(x - 8)$

6. $y = (x^4 + 2x^3 + 12)^5$

7. $y = 8^{6x}$

8. $y = \text{Ln}(6x^2 - 5x + 2)$

9. $f(x) = \dfrac{x^2 - 5x}{4x^3 + 3x^2 + 12}$

10. $f(x) = \log_3(x^2 - 12x)$

11. $y = \dfrac{4}{\sqrt[3]{x}}$

12. $y = 8 \cos x^4$

13. $f(x) = \sqrt{x}\, e^{x-2}$

14. $f(x) = (\csc x + \cot x)^6$

15. $y = \text{Ln}\, 10$

16. Using the definition of the derivative $f'(x) = \lim\limits_{\Delta x \to 0} \dfrac{f(x + \Delta x) - f(x)}{\Delta x}$
   find the derivative of $f(x) = 7x^2 - x$.

17. $\lim\limits_{x \to 6}(2x + 3) =$

18. Given that $y = e^{\sqrt{x}}$, find the differential element dy.

19. Implicitly differentiate $x^3 y^2 + e^{xy} = \sin x^2$.

20. Given that $y = x^5 - \cos 2x$, find $\dfrac{d^3 y}{dx^3}$.

Integrate each of the following:

21. $\displaystyle\int x^2\,dx$

22. $\displaystyle\int_{2}^{5} 3x\,dx$

23. $\displaystyle\int e^{2x}\,dx$

24. $\displaystyle\int \sin x\,dx$

25. $\displaystyle\int \left(\frac{1}{x^2} + \frac{1}{\sqrt{x}}\right) dx$

26. Integrate $\displaystyle\int \left(3x^2 - 4\right)\left(x^3 - 4x + 8\right)^6 dx$ using the method of substitution.

27. Integrate $\displaystyle\int xe^{5x}\,dx$ using integration by parts.

28. Integrate $\displaystyle\int \frac{dx}{\sqrt{16 - 49x^2}}$ using trigonometric substitution.

29. Use the Trapezoidal Rule to approximate the given integral.

$$\int_{0}^{1} x^2\,dx; \qquad n = 5$$

30. Find the volume of the figure generated by rotating the function $f(x) = 2x + 3$ about the x-axis between the endpoints $x = 0$ and $x = 4$.

31. Integrate the function $\displaystyle\int \sqrt{144 - x^2}\ dx$ using the Table of Integrals on page #   .

32. Given that $y = x^2 z^3 + \sqrt{xz}$, find $\dfrac{\partial y}{\partial x}, \dfrac{\partial y}{\partial z}, \dfrac{\partial^2 y}{\partial x^2}$, and $\dfrac{\partial^2 y}{\partial z^2}$.

33. Use Simpson's Rule with $n = 8$ to approximate the integral $\displaystyle\int_{2}^{4} x^4\,dx$.

34. Determine which of the following are functions :

a) $\{(1, -1), (6, 2), (1, -2)\}$

b) $y = x^3$

c)

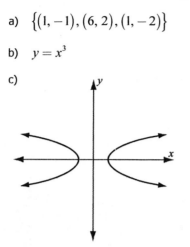

35. Find the slope of the line that passes through the points $(-1, 6)$ and $(0, -4)$.

36. Find the slope of the line that is tangent to the curve $f(x) = x^3$ at $x = -2$.

37. Find any/all maxima, minima, and points of inflection for the function $f(x) = x^2 - 3x$.

38. Given that $y = \dfrac{u}{2} + \sqrt{u}$ and $u = \cos 5x$, find $\dfrac{dy}{du}$, $\dfrac{du}{dx}$, and $\dfrac{dy}{dx}$.

39. Solve the given differential equation.

$$y^3 \frac{dy}{dx} = e^{6x}$$

40. Evaluate the given double integral.

$$\int_1^2 \int_0^1 \left(x^2 + y^3\right) dx\, dy$$

1. $f'(x) = 2x + 6$

2. $\dfrac{dy}{dx} = (4 + 3x)(14x - 8) + (7x^2 - 8x + 2)(3)$

3. $\dfrac{dy}{dx} = 27x^2 e^{9x^3}$

4. $f'(x) = 3x^2 \cos x^3$

5. $f'(x) = \sec^2(x - 8)$

6. $\dfrac{dy}{dx} = 5(x^4 + 2x^3 + 12)^4 (4x^3 + 6x)$

7. $\dfrac{dy}{dx} = 6 \cdot \text{Ln } 8 \cdot 8^{6x}$

8. $\dfrac{dy}{dx} = \dfrac{12x - 5}{6x^2 - 5x + 2}$

9. $f'(x) = \dfrac{(4x^3 + 3x^2 + 12)(2x - 5) - (x^2 - 5x)(12x^2 + 6x)}{(4x^3 + 3x^2 + 12)^2}$

10. $f'(x) = \dfrac{2x - 12}{x^2 - 12x} \cdot \dfrac{1}{\text{Ln } 3}$

11. $\dfrac{dy}{dx} = -\dfrac{4}{3x\sqrt[3]{x}}$

12. $\dfrac{dy}{dx} = -8(4x^3)\sin x^4 = -32x^3 \sin x^4$

13. $f'(x) = \sqrt{x}\, e^{x-2} + \dfrac{e^{x-2}}{2\sqrt{x}}$

14. $f'(x) = 6(\csc x + \cot x)^5 (-\csc x \cot x - \csc^2 x)$

15. $\dfrac{dy}{dx} = 0$

16. $f'(x) = 14x - 1$

17. $\lim\limits_{x \to 6}(2x + 3) = 15$

18. $dy = \dfrac{1}{2\sqrt{x}} e^{\sqrt{x}}\, dx$

19. $\dfrac{dy}{dx} = \dfrac{2x \cos x^2 - 3x^2 y^2 - y e^{xy}}{2x^3 y + x e^{xy}}$

20. $\dfrac{d^3 y}{dx^3} = 60x^2 - 8 \sin 2x$

21. $\displaystyle\int x^2\,dx = \frac{1}{3}x^3 + C$

22. $\displaystyle\int_{2}^{5} 3x\,dx = 31\frac{1}{2}$

23. $\displaystyle\int e^{2x}\,dx = \frac{1}{2}e^{2x} + C$

24. $\displaystyle\int \sin x\,dx = -\cos x + C$

25. $\displaystyle\int \left(\frac{1}{x^2} + \frac{1}{\sqrt{x}}\right)dx = -\frac{1}{x} + 2\sqrt{x} + C$

26. $\displaystyle\int \left(3x^2 - 4\right)\left(x^3 - 4x + 8\right)^6 dx = \frac{1}{7}\left(x^3 - 4x + 8\right)^7 + C$

27. $\displaystyle\int xe^{5x}\,dx = \frac{1}{5}xe^{5x} - \frac{1}{25}e^{5x} + C$

28. $\displaystyle\int \frac{dx}{\sqrt{16 - 49x^2}} = \frac{1}{7}\arcsin\frac{7x}{4} + C$

29. $\displaystyle\int_{0}^{1} x^2\,dx \approx 0.34$

30. $V = \dfrac{652}{3}\pi \approx 682.77$

31. $\displaystyle\int \sqrt{144 - x^2}\,dx = \frac{x}{2}\sqrt{144 - x^2} + 72\sin^{-1}\frac{x}{a} + C$

32. $\dfrac{\partial y}{\partial x} = 2xz^3 + \dfrac{\sqrt{z}}{2\sqrt{x}}$

$\dfrac{\partial^2 y}{\partial x^2} = 2z^3 - \dfrac{\sqrt{z}}{4x\sqrt{x}}$

$\dfrac{\partial y}{\partial z} = 3x^2z^2 + \dfrac{\sqrt{x}}{2\sqrt{x}}$

$\dfrac{\partial^2 y}{\partial z^2} = 6x^2z - \dfrac{\sqrt{x}}{4z\sqrt{z}}$

33. $\displaystyle\int_{2}^{4} x^4\,dx \approx 198.4010$

34.

   a) Not a function

   b) Function

   c) Not a function

35. Slope $= -10$

36. Slope $= 12$

37. A local minimum occurs at $x = \dfrac{3}{2}$

38. $\dfrac{dy}{du} = \dfrac{1}{2} + \dfrac{1}{2\sqrt{u}}$

$\dfrac{du}{dx} = -5\sin x$

$\dfrac{dy}{dx} = \left(\dfrac{1}{2} + \dfrac{1}{2\sqrt{\cos 5x}} \right)(-5\sin x)$

39. $y = \sqrt[4]{\dfrac{2}{3}e^{6x} + C}$

40. $\displaystyle\int_{1}^{2}\int_{0}^{1}\left(x^2 + y^3\right)dx\,dy = 4\dfrac{7}{12}$

1. $f(x) = x^2 + 6x - 5$

    $f'(x) = 2x + 6$

2. $y = (4 + 3x)(7x^2 - 8x + 2)$

    Using the Product Rule,

    $\dfrac{dy}{dx} = (4 + 3x)(14x - 8) + (7x^2 - 8x + 2)(3)$

3. $y = e^{9x^3}$

    $\dfrac{dy}{dx} = 27x^2 e^{9x^3}$

4. $f(x) = \sin x^3$

    $f'(x) = 3x^2 \cos x^3$

5. $f(x) = \tan(x - 8)$

    $f'(x) = (1)\sec^2(x - 8)$

    $f'(x) = \sec^2(x - 8)$

6. $y = (x^4 + 2x^3 + 12)^5$

    $\dfrac{dy}{dx} = 5(x^4 + 2x^3 + 12)^4 (4x^3 + 6x)$

7. $y = 8^{6x}$

    $\dfrac{dy}{dx} = 6 \cdot \text{Ln}\, 8 \cdot 8^{6x}$

8. $y = \text{Ln}(6x^2 - 5x + 2)$

    $\dfrac{dy}{dx} = \dfrac{12x - 5}{6x^2 - 5x + 2}$

9. $f(x) = \dfrac{x^2 - 5x}{4x^3 + 3x^2 + 12}$

    Using the Quotient Rule,

    $f'(x) = \dfrac{(4x^3 + 3x^2 + 12)(2x - 5) - (x^2 - 5x)(12x^2 + 6x)}{(4x^3 + 3x^2 + 12)^2}$

10. $f(x) = \log_3\left(x^2 - 12x\right)$

$$f'(x) = (2x - 12) \cdot \frac{1}{\text{Ln}\,3}\left(\frac{1}{x^2 - 12x}\right)$$

$$f'(x) = \frac{2x - 12}{x^2 - 12x} \cdot \frac{1}{\text{Ln}\,3}$$

11. $y = \dfrac{4}{\sqrt[3]{x}} = \dfrac{4}{x^{\frac{1}{3}}} = 4x^{-\frac{1}{3}}$

$$\frac{dy}{dx} = \left(-\frac{1}{3}\right)\left(4x^{-\frac{4}{3}}\right)$$

$$\frac{dy}{dx} = -\frac{4}{3x^{\frac{4}{3}}}$$

$$\frac{dy}{dx} = -\frac{4}{3x\sqrt[3]{x}}$$

12. $y = 8\cos x^4$

$$\frac{dy}{dx} = -8\left(4x^3\right)\sin x^4 = -32x^3 \sin x^4$$

13. $f(x) = \sqrt{x}\,e^{x-2} = x^{\frac{1}{2}} \cdot e^{x-2}$

Using the Product Rule,

$$f'(x) = x^{\frac{1}{2}}e^{x-2} + e^{x-2}\left(\frac{1}{2}x^{-\frac{1}{2}}\right)$$

$$f'(x) = \sqrt{x}\,e^{x-2} + \frac{e^{x-2}}{2\sqrt{x}}$$

14. $f(x) = \left(\csc x + \cot x\right)^6$

$$f'(x) = 6\left(\csc x + \cot x\right)^5\left(-\csc x \cot x - \csc^2 x\right)$$

15. $y = \text{Ln}\,10$

Since Ln 10 is simply a constant, $\dfrac{dy}{dx} = 0.$

16. $f(x) = 7x^2 - x$

$$f'(x) = \lim_{\Delta x \to 0} \frac{f(x + \Delta x) - f(x)}{\Delta x}$$

$$f'(x) = \lim_{\Delta x \to 0} \frac{\left[7(x + \Delta x)^2 - (x + \Delta x)\right] - (7x^2 - x)}{\Delta x}$$

$$f'(x) = \lim_{\Delta x \to 0} \frac{7\left[x^2 + 2x\Delta x + (\Delta x)^2\right] - x - \Delta x - 7x^2 + x}{\Delta x}$$

$$f'(x) = \lim_{\Delta x \to 0} \frac{7x^2 + 14x\Delta x + 7(\Delta x)^2 - \Delta x - 7x^2}{\Delta x}$$

$$f'(x) = \lim_{\Delta x \to 0} \frac{14x\Delta x + 7(\Delta x)^2 - \Delta x}{\Delta x}$$

$$f'(x) = \lim_{\Delta x \to 0} \frac{\Delta x(14x + 7\Delta x - 1)}{\Delta x}$$

$$f'(x) = \lim_{\Delta x \to 0} (14x + 7\Delta x - 1)$$

$$f'(x) = \lim_{\Delta x \to 0} 14x - 1$$

17. $\lim_{x \to 6} (2x + 3) = 2(6) + 3 = 15$

18. $y = e^{\sqrt{x}} = e^{x^{\frac{1}{2}}}$

$$\frac{dy}{dx} = \frac{1}{2} x^{-\frac{1}{2}} e^{x^{\frac{1}{2}}} = \frac{1}{2\sqrt{x}} e^{\sqrt{x}}$$

$$dy = \frac{1}{2\sqrt{x}} e^{\sqrt{x}} dx$$

19. $x^3 y^2 + e^{xy} = \sin x^2$

$$x^3 \left(2y \frac{dy}{dx}\right) + y^2 (3x^2) + \left(x \frac{dy}{dx} + y\right) e^{xy} = 2x \cos x^2$$

$$2x^3 y \frac{dy}{dx} + 3x^2 y^2 + xe^{xy} \frac{dy}{dx} + ye^{xy} = 2x \cos x^2$$

$$2x^3 y \frac{dy}{dx} + xe^{xy} \frac{dy}{dx} = 2x \cos x^2 - 3x^2 y^2 - ye^{xy}$$

$$\frac{dy}{dx}(2x^3 y + xe^{xy}) = 2x \cos x^2 - 3x^2 y^2 - ye^{xy}$$

$$\frac{dy}{dx} = \frac{2x \cos x^2 - 3x^2 y^2 - ye^{xy}}{2x^3 y + xe^{xy}}$$

20. $y = x^5 - \cos 2x$

$$\frac{dy}{dx} = 5x^4 - (-2\sin 2x) = 5x^4 + 2\sin 2x$$

$$\frac{d^2 y}{dx^2} = 20x^3 + 4\cos 2x$$

$$\frac{d^3 y}{dx^3} = 60x^2 - 8\sin 2x$$

21. $\displaystyle\int x^2\, dx = \frac{1}{3}x^3 + C$

22. $\displaystyle\int_2^5 3x\, dx = \left[\frac{3}{2}x^2\right]_2^5$

$$= \frac{3}{2}(5)^2 - \frac{3}{2}(2)^2$$

$$= \frac{75}{2} - 6$$

$$= 31\frac{1}{2}$$

23. $\displaystyle\int e^{2x}\, dx = \frac{1}{2}e^{2x} + C$

24. $\displaystyle\int \sin x\, dx = -\cos x + C$

25. $\displaystyle\int \left(\frac{1}{x^2} + \frac{1}{\sqrt{x}}\right) dx = \int \left(x^{-2} + x^{-\frac{1}{2}}\right) dx$

$$= -x^{-1} + 2x^{\frac{1}{2}} + C$$

$$= -\frac{1}{x} + 2\sqrt{x} + C$$

26. $\int \left(3x^2 - 4\right)\left(x^3 - 4x + 8\right)^6 dx = \int \left(x^3 - 4x + 8\right)^6 \left(3x^2 - 4\right) dx$

$u = x^3 - 4x + 8$

$\dfrac{du}{dx} = 3x^2 - 4$

$du = \left(3x^2 - 4\right) dx$

$\Rightarrow \quad \int \left(x^3 - 4x + 8\right)^6 \left(3x^2 - 4\right) dx = \int u^6 du$

Integrating:

$\int u^6 du = \dfrac{1}{7} u^7 + C$

Reinserting the original expression for u:

$\int \left(3x^2 - 4\right)\left(x^3 - 4x + 8\right)^6 dx = \dfrac{1}{7}\left(x^3 - 4x + 8\right)^7 + C$

27. $\int \underset{\substack{\uparrow \\ u \quad dv}}{xe^{5x} dx}$

$u = x \qquad\qquad dv = e^{5x} dx$

$\dfrac{du}{dx} = 1 \qquad\qquad \dfrac{dv}{dx} = e^{5x}$

$du = dx \qquad\qquad v = \dfrac{1}{5} e^{5x}$

$\int u\,dv = uv - \int v\,du$

$\int xe^{5x} dx = x\left(\dfrac{1}{5} e^{5x}\right) - \int \dfrac{1}{5} e^{5x} dx$

$\int xe^{5x} dx = \dfrac{1}{5} xe^{5x} - \int \dfrac{1}{5} e^{5x} dx$

$\int xe^{5x} dx = \dfrac{1}{5} xe^{5x} - \dfrac{1}{25} e^{5x} + C$

28. $\displaystyle\int \frac{dx}{\sqrt{16-49x^2}}$

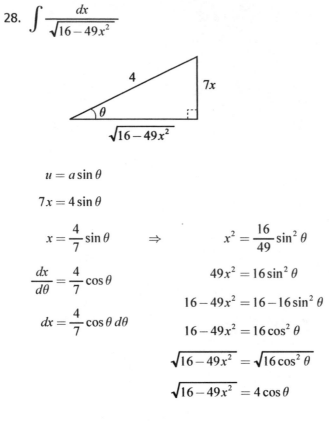

$u = a\sin\theta$

$7x = 4\sin\theta$

$x = \dfrac{4}{7}\sin\theta \qquad \Rightarrow \qquad x^2 = \dfrac{16}{49}\sin^2\theta$

$\dfrac{dx}{d\theta} = \dfrac{4}{7}\cos\theta \qquad\qquad 49x^2 = 16\sin^2\theta$

$\qquad\qquad\qquad\qquad 16 - 49x^2 = 16 - 16\sin^2\theta$

$dx = \dfrac{4}{7}\cos\theta\, d\theta \qquad 16 - 49x^2 = 16\cos^2\theta$

$\qquad\qquad\qquad\qquad \sqrt{16-49x^2} = \sqrt{16\cos^2\theta}$

$\qquad\qquad\qquad\qquad \sqrt{16-49x^2} = 4\cos\theta$

$\Rightarrow \displaystyle\int \frac{dx}{\sqrt{16-49x^2}} = \int \frac{\dfrac{4}{7}\cos\,d\theta}{4\cos\theta}$

$\qquad\qquad\qquad = \displaystyle\int \frac{1}{7}\,d\theta$

$\qquad\qquad\qquad = \dfrac{1}{7}\theta + C$

From the triangle, $\theta = \arcsin\dfrac{7x}{4}$

$\Rightarrow \displaystyle\int \frac{dx}{\sqrt{16-49x^2}} = \frac{1}{7}\arcsin\frac{7x}{4} + C$

29. $\displaystyle\int_0^1 x^2\,dx;\quad n=5$

$$h = \frac{b-a}{n}$$

$$h = \frac{1-0}{5}$$

$$h = \frac{1}{5} = 0.2$$

$\Rightarrow$ $x_0 = 0.0$ $f(x_0) = f(0.0) = (0.0)^2 = 0.00$

$x_1 = 0.2$ $f(x_1) = f(0.2) = (0.2)^2 = 0.04$

$x_2 = 0.4$ $f(x_2) = f(0.4) = (0.4)^2 = 0.16$

$x_3 = 0.6$ $f(x_3) = f(0.6) = (0.6)^2 = 0.36$

$x_4 = 0.8$ $f(x_4) = f(0.8) = (0.8)^2 = 0.64$

$x_5 = 1.0$ $f(x_5) = f(1.0) = (1.0)^2 = 1.00$

$$\int_0^1 x^2\,dx \approx \frac{0.2}{2}\left[0.00 + 2(0.04) + 2(0.16) + 2(0.36) + 2(0.64) + 1.00\right]$$

$$\int_0^1 x^2\,dx \approx \frac{0.2}{2}(0 + 0.08 + 0.32 + 0.72 + 1.28 + 1)$$

$$\int_0^1 x^2\,dx \approx \frac{0.2}{2}(3.4)$$

$$\int_0^1 x^2\,dx \approx 0.34$$

30. $f(x) = 2x + 3;$ $\qquad x = 0$ and $x = 4$

$$V = \int_0^4 \pi \left[f(x) \right]^2 dx$$

$$V = \int_0^4 \pi (2x + 3)^2 dx$$

$$V = \int_0^4 \pi \left(4x^2 + 12x + 9 \right) dx$$

$$V = \left[\pi \left(\frac{4}{3} x^3 + 6x^2 + 9x \right) \right]_0^4$$

$$V = \left[\pi \left(\frac{4}{3}(4)^3 + 6(4)^2 + 9(4) \right) \right] - \left[\pi \left(\frac{4}{3}(0)^3 + 6(0)^2 + 9(0) \right) \right]$$

$$V = \pi \left(\frac{256}{3} + 96 + 36 \right) - 0$$

$$V = \frac{652}{3} \pi \approx 682.77$$

31. Using integral form #29 :

$$\int \sqrt{144 - x^2} \; dx = \frac{x}{2} \sqrt{144 - x^2} + \frac{144}{2} \sin^{-1} \frac{x}{a} + C$$

$$= \frac{x}{2} \sqrt{144 - x^2} + 72 \sin^{-1} \frac{x}{a} + C$$

32. $y = x^2 z^3 + \sqrt{xz}$

$\quad y = x^2 z^3 + \sqrt{x} \cdot \sqrt{z}$

$\quad y = x^2 z^3 + x^{\frac{1}{2}} \cdot z^{\frac{1}{2}}$

$$\frac{\partial y}{\partial x} = 2xz^3 + \frac{1}{2} x^{-\frac{1}{2}} \cdot z^{\frac{1}{2}} = 2xz^3 + \frac{\sqrt{z}}{2\sqrt{x}}$$

$$\frac{\partial^2 y}{\partial x^2} = 2z^3 - \frac{1}{4} x^{-\frac{3}{2}} \cdot z^{\frac{1}{2}} = 2z^3 - \frac{\sqrt{z}}{4x\sqrt{x}}$$

$$\frac{\partial y}{\partial z} = 3x^2 z^2 + x^{\frac{1}{2}} \left(\frac{1}{2} z^{-\frac{1}{2}} \right) = 3x^2 z^2 + \frac{\sqrt{x}}{2\sqrt{x}}$$

$$\frac{\partial^2 y}{\partial z^2} = 6x^2 z + x^{\frac{1}{2}} \left(-\frac{1}{4} z^{-\frac{3}{2}} \right) = 6x^2 z - \frac{\sqrt{x}}{4z\sqrt{z}}$$

33. $\displaystyle\int_2^4 x^4\,dx; \quad n = 8$

$$h = \frac{b-a}{n}$$

$$h = \frac{4-2}{8}$$

$$h = \frac{2}{8} = 0.25$$

$\Rightarrow \quad x_0 = 2.00 \qquad f(x_0) = f(2.00) = (2.00)^4 = 16.0000$

$\qquad x_1 = 2.25 \qquad f(x_1) = f(2.25) = (2.25)^4 \approx 25.6289$

$\qquad x_2 = 2.50 \qquad f(x_2) = f(2.50) = (2.50)^4 = 39.0625$

$\qquad x_3 = 2.75 \qquad f(x_3) = f(2.75) = (2.75)^4 \approx 57.1914$

$\qquad x_4 = 3.00 \qquad f(x_4) = f(3.00) = (3.00)^4 = 81.0000$

$\qquad x_5 = 3.25 \qquad f(x_5) = f(3.25) = (3.25)^4 \approx 111.5664$

$\qquad x_6 = 3.50 \qquad f(x_6) = f(3.50) = (3.50)^4 = 150.0625$

$\qquad x_7 = 3.75 \qquad f(x_7) = f(3.75) = (3.75)^4 \approx 197.7539$

$\qquad x_8 = 4.00 \qquad f(x_8) = f(4.00) = (4.00)^4 = 256.0000$

$$\int_2^4 x^4\,dx \approx \frac{0.25}{3}\left[\begin{array}{l}16.0000 + 4(25.6289) + 2(39.0625) + 4(57.1914) + 2(81.0000) + 4(111.5664) \\ +2(150.0625) + 4(197.7539) + 256.0000\end{array}\right]$$

$$\int_2^4 x^4\,dx \approx \frac{0.25}{3}\left(\begin{array}{l}16.0000 + 102.5156 + 78.1250 + 228.7656 + 162.0000 + 446.2656 + 300.1250 \\ +791.0156 + 256.0000\end{array}\right)$$

$$\int_2^4 x^4\,dx \approx \frac{0.25}{3}(2380.8124)$$

$$\int_2^4 x^4\,dx \approx 198.4010$$

34.

a) $\{(1, -1), (6, 2), (1, -2)\}$

Domain $= \{1, 6\}$

Range $= \{-2, -1, 2\}$

The domain element 1 is associated with two different range elements (-1 and -2). Therefore, the relation is *not* a function.

b) $y = x^3$

Each x-value is associated with a single y-value. The equation is therefore a function.

c)

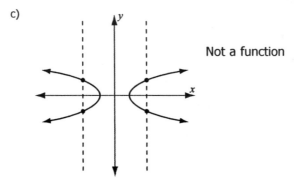

Not a function

35. $(-1, 6) \ (0, -4)$

$$\text{Slope} = \frac{y_2 - y_1}{x_2 - x_1}$$

$$= \frac{-4 - 6}{0 - (-1)}$$

$$= \frac{-10}{1}$$

$$= -10$$

36. $f(x) = x^3$

$$f'(x) = 3x^2$$

$$f'(-2) = 3(-2)^2 = 12$$

The slope of the tangent line at $x = -2$ is 12.

37. $f(x) = x^2 - 3x$

$f'(x) = 2x - 3$

$2x - 3 = 0$

$2x = 3$

$x = \dfrac{3}{2}$

Point of interest: $x = \dfrac{3}{2}$

$f''(x) = 2$

$\Rightarrow\ f''\left(\dfrac{3}{2}\right) = 2 > 0 \quad \Rightarrow \quad$ a relative minimum occurs at $x = \dfrac{3}{2}$

38. $y = \dfrac{u}{2} + \sqrt{u}\,; \qquad u = \cos 5x$

$y = \dfrac{1}{2}u + u^{\frac{1}{2}}$

$\dfrac{dy}{du} = \dfrac{1}{2} + \dfrac{1}{2}u^{-\frac{1}{2}} = \dfrac{1}{2} + \dfrac{1}{2\sqrt{u}}$

$\dfrac{du}{dx} = -5\sin 5x$

$\dfrac{dy}{dx} = \dfrac{dy}{du} \cdot \dfrac{du}{dx}$

$\dfrac{dy}{dx} = \left(\dfrac{1}{2} + \dfrac{1}{2\sqrt{u}}\right) \cdot (-5\sin 5x)$

$\dfrac{dy}{dx} = \left(\dfrac{1}{2} + \dfrac{1}{2\sqrt{\cos 5x}}\right)(-5\sin 5x)$

39. $y^3 \dfrac{dy}{dx} = e^{6x}$

$$y^3 \dfrac{dy}{dx} \cdot dx = e^{6x} \cdot dx$$

$$y^3 dy = e^{6x} dx$$

$$\int y^3 dy = \int e^{6x} dx$$

$$\frac{1}{4} y^4 = \frac{1}{6} e^{6x} + C$$

$$y^4 = \frac{2}{3} e^{6x} + C$$

$$\sqrt[4]{y^4} = \sqrt[4]{\frac{2}{3} e^{6x} + C}$$

$$y = \sqrt[4]{\frac{2}{3} e^{6x} + C}$$

40. $\displaystyle\int_1^2 \int_0^1 \left(x^2 + y^3\right) dx\,dy$

Evaluating the inner integral with respect to dx:

$$\int_0^1 \left(x^2 + y^3\right) dx = \left[\frac{1}{3} x^3 + xy^3 \right]_0^1$$

$$= \left[\frac{1}{3}(1)^3 + (1)y^3 \right] - \left[\frac{1}{3}(0)^3 + (0)y^3 \right]$$

$$= \frac{1}{3} + y^3$$

$$\Rightarrow \int_1^2 \int_0^1 \left(x^2 + y^3\right) dx\,dy = \int_1^2 \left(\frac{1}{3} + y^3 \right) dy$$

Finally,

$$\int_1^2 \left(\frac{1}{3} + y^3 \right) dy = \left[\frac{1}{3} y + \frac{1}{4} y^4 \right]_1^2$$

$$= \left[\frac{1}{3}(2) + \frac{1}{4}(2)^4 \right] - \left[\frac{1}{3}(1) + \frac{1}{4}(1)^4 \right]$$

$$= \left(\frac{2}{3} + 4 \right) - \left(\frac{1}{3} + \frac{1}{4} \right)$$

$$= \frac{55}{12} = 4\frac{7}{12}$$

$$\Rightarrow \int_1^2 \int_0^1 \left(x^2 + y^3\right) dx\,dy = 4\frac{7}{12}$$

Final
Examination II

Find the derivative of each of the following.

1. $f(x) = e^{\frac{1}{x} - \frac{1}{x^2}}$

2. $f(x) = \sin\left(\operatorname{Ln} x^3\right)$

3. $y = \left[\cos\left(x^2 - 5x\right) + x^3\right]\left(\dfrac{2}{\sqrt{x}} + \dfrac{\tan 3x}{8}\right)$

4. $y = 3^{4.7x^2}$

5. $f(x) = \dfrac{e + x^6}{\csc x^4 - \sec x^3}$

6. Find the slope of the line that passes throught the origin and is perpendicular to the line $y = \dfrac{1}{5}x + 6$.

7. $\lim\limits_{x \to 3} \dfrac{x^3 - 27}{x - 3} =$

8. Find the volume of the figure generated by rotating $f(x) = \sin x$ about the x-axis between the endpoints $x = 0$ and $x = \pi$.

9. Given that $y = \tan\left(\sqrt[3]{u} + u\right)$ and $u = e^{2-x} + \operatorname{Ln} x$, find $\dfrac{dy}{dx}$.

Integrate each of the following.

10. $\displaystyle\int_{0}^{\frac{\pi}{2}} (\sin x + \cos x)\, dx$

11. $\displaystyle\int \dfrac{5}{e^{6x}}\, dx$

12. $\displaystyle\int_{-1}^{4} \dfrac{x^2 - x - 6}{x - 3}\, dx$

13. $\displaystyle\int \sec^2 5x\, dx$

14. $\displaystyle\int \dfrac{dx}{\sqrt{x - 7}}\, dx$

15. Integrate the function $\displaystyle\int \dfrac{\sin^3 x}{8}\, dx$ using the Table of Integrals on page   .

16. Integrate the function $\displaystyle\int_{0}^{\frac{\pi}{4}} 2x \cos x\, dx$ using integration by parts.

17. Implicitly differentiate $\cos x^2 y + \sqrt{x^2 + y^2} = e^{x+y}$.

18. Use Simpson's Rule with $n = 8$ to approximate the integral $\displaystyle\int_1^3 \frac{1}{x}\, dx$.

19. Integrate $\displaystyle\int \frac{x^2}{\sqrt{x^2 - 100}}\, dx$ using trigonometric substitution.

20. Integrate $\displaystyle\int \frac{4x - 3}{\sqrt{4x^2 - 6x + 3}}\, dx$ using the method of substitution.

21. Given that $y = x^3 z w^4 + e^{xwz}$, find $\dfrac{\partial y}{\partial x}, \dfrac{\partial y}{\partial z}$, and $\dfrac{\partial y}{\partial w}$.

22. Given that $y = x^5 + e^{x-2} + \sin\left(x^2 - 7x + 3\right)$, find $\dfrac{d^2 y}{dx^2}$.

23. Using the Trapezoidal Rule, approximate the integral $\displaystyle\int_1^6 2x^2\, dx; \quad n = 10$.

24. Using the definition of the derivative $f'(x) = \displaystyle\lim_{\Delta x \to 0} \frac{f(x + \Delta x) - f(x)}{\Delta x}$

    find the derivative of $f(x) = \dfrac{3}{x}$.

25. Find the particular solution to the given differential equation using the given initial conditions.
$$\cos^2 x \frac{dy}{dx} - 2 = 0; \quad y = -11 \text{ when } x = \frac{\pi}{4}$$

26. Find any/all maxima, minima, and points of inflection for the function
$$f(x) = \frac{1}{3} x^3 - 4x + 6.$$

27. Find the slope of the line that is tangent to the function $f(x) = 2e^{10x}$ at $x = 0$.

28. Determine which of the following are functions :

    a) $y^2 = x$

    b)

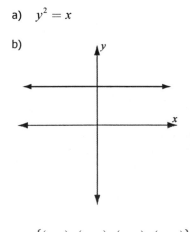

    c) $\{(1, 6), (2, 6), (3, 6), (4, 6)\}$

29. Given that $y = \tan \sqrt{x^3 - 3}$, find the differential element dy.

30. Evaluate the given triple integral.

$$\int_{-3}^{2} \int_{0}^{2} \int_{-1}^{1} (x + y - z) \, dz \, dx \, dy$$

1. $f'(x) = \left(-\dfrac{1}{x^2} + \dfrac{2}{x^3}\right) e^{\frac{1}{x} - \frac{1}{x^2}}$

2. $f'(x) = \dfrac{3}{x} \cos\left(\text{Ln } x^3\right)$

3. $\dfrac{dy}{dx} = \left[\cos\left(x^2 - 5x\right) + x^3\right]\left[-\dfrac{1}{x\sqrt{x}} + \dfrac{3}{8}\sec^2 3x\right] + \left(\dfrac{2}{\sqrt{x}} + \dfrac{1}{8}\tan 3x\right)\left[-(2x-5)\sin\left(x^2 - 5x\right) + 3x^2\right]$

4. $\dfrac{dy}{dx} = 9.4x \cdot \text{Ln } 3 \cdot 3^{4.7x^2}$

5. $f'(x) = \dfrac{\left(\csc x^4 - \sec x^3\right)\left(6x^5\right) - \left(e + x^6\right)\left(-4x^3 \csc x^4 \cot x^4 - 3x^2 \sec x^3 \tan x^3\right)}{\left(\csc x^4 - \sec x^3\right)^2}$

6. slope $= -5$

7. $\lim\limits_{x \to 3} \dfrac{x^3 - 27}{x - 3} = 27$

8. $V = \dfrac{1}{2}\pi^2 \approx 4.93$

9. $\dfrac{dy}{dx} = \left(\dfrac{1}{3\sqrt[3]{\left(e^{2-x} + \text{Ln } x\right)^2}} + 1\right)\sec^2\left(\sqrt[3]{e^{2-x} + \text{Ln } x} + e^{2-x} + \text{Ln } x\right)\left(-e^{2-x} + \dfrac{1}{x}\right)$

10. $\displaystyle\int_0^{\frac{\pi}{2}} \left(\sin x + \cos x\right) dx = 2$

11. $\displaystyle\int \dfrac{5}{e^{6x}}\, dx = -\dfrac{5}{6e^{6x}} + C$

12. $\displaystyle\int_{-1}^{4} \dfrac{x^2 - x - 6}{x - 3}\, dx = 17\dfrac{1}{2}$

13. $\displaystyle\int \sec^2 5x\, dx = \dfrac{1}{5}\tan 5x + C$

14. $\displaystyle\int \dfrac{dx}{\sqrt{x - 7}}\, dx = 2\sqrt{x - 7} + C$

15. $\displaystyle\int \dfrac{\sin^3 x}{8}\, dx = -\dfrac{1}{24}\left(2 + \sin^2 x\right)\cos x + C$

16. $\displaystyle\int_0^{\frac{\pi}{4}} 2x \cos x\, dx = \dfrac{\sqrt{2}\,\pi}{4} + \sqrt{2} - 2 \approx 0.52$

17. $\dfrac{dy}{dx} = \dfrac{e^{x+y} + 2xy\sin x^2 y - \dfrac{x}{\sqrt{x^2+y^2}}}{\left(-x^2\sin x^2 y + \dfrac{y}{\sqrt{x^2+y^2}} - e^{x+y}\right)}$

18. $\displaystyle\int_1^3 \frac{1}{x}\,dx \approx 1.0987$

19. $\displaystyle\int \frac{x^2}{\sqrt{x^2-100}}\,dx = \frac{x\sqrt{x^2-100}}{2} + 50\,\mathrm{Ln}\left|x+\sqrt{x^2-100}\right| - 50\,\mathrm{Ln}\,|10| + C$

20. $\displaystyle\int \frac{4x-3}{\sqrt{4x^2-6x+3}}\,dx = \sqrt{4x^2-6x+3} + C$

21. $\dfrac{\partial y}{\partial x} = 3x^2 zw^4 + wze^{xwz}$

$\dfrac{\partial y}{\partial z} = x^3 w^4 + xwe^{xwz}$

$\dfrac{\partial y}{\partial w} = 4x^3 zw^3 + xze^{xwz}$

22. $\dfrac{d^2 y}{dx^2} = 20x^3 + e^{x-2} - (2x-7)^2 \sin(x^2-7x+3) + 2\cos(x^2-7x+3)$

23. $\displaystyle\int_1^6 2x^2\,dx \approx 161.8$

24. $f'(x) = -\dfrac{3}{x^2}$

25. $y = 2\tan x - 9$

26.

$f''(-2) = 2(-2) = -4 < 0 \quad \Rightarrow \quad$ a relative maximum occurs at $x = -2$.

$f''(2) = 2(2) = 4 > 0 \quad \Rightarrow \quad$ a relative minimum occurs at $x = 2$.

27. The slope of the tangent line at $x = 0$ is 20.

28.
   a) Not a Function
   b) Function
   c) Function

29. $dy = \dfrac{3x^2}{2\sqrt{x^3-3}}\sec^2\sqrt{x^3-3}$

30. $\displaystyle\int_{-3}^2\int_0^2\int_{-1}^1 (x+y-z)\,dz\,dx\,dy = 10$

1. $f(x) = e^{\frac{1}{x} - \frac{1}{x^2}} = e^{x^{-1} - x^{-2}}$

$f'(x) = \left[-x^{-2} - \left(-2x^{-3} \right) \right] e^{x^{-1} - x^{-2}}$

$f'(x) = \left(-\dfrac{1}{x^2} + \dfrac{2}{x^3} \right) e^{x^{-1} - x^{-2}}$

$f'(x) = \left(-\dfrac{1}{x^2} + \dfrac{2}{x^3} \right) e^{\frac{1}{x} - \frac{1}{x^2}}$

2. $f(x) = \sin\left(\operatorname{Ln} x^3 \right)$

$f'(x) = \left(\dfrac{3x^2}{x^3} \right) \cos\left(\operatorname{Ln} x^3 \right)$

$f'(x) = \dfrac{3}{x} \cos\left(\operatorname{Ln} x^3 \right)$

3. $y = \left[\cos\left(x^2 - 5x \right) + x^3 \right] \left(\dfrac{2}{\sqrt{x}} + \dfrac{\tan 3x}{8} \right)$

$y = \left[\cos\left(x^2 - 5x \right) + x^3 \right] \left(2x^{-\frac{1}{2}} + \dfrac{1}{8} \tan 3x \right)$

Using the Product Rule,

$\dfrac{dy}{dx} = \left[\cos\left(x^2 - 5x \right) + x^3 \right] \left[-\dfrac{1}{2} \left(2x^{-\frac{3}{2}} \right) + \dfrac{1}{8}(3) \sec^2 3x \right]$

$\qquad + \left(2x^{-\frac{1}{2}} + \dfrac{1}{8} \tan 3x \right) \left[-(2x - 5) \sin\left(x^2 - 5x \right) + 3x^2 \right]$

$\dfrac{dy}{dx} = \left[\cos\left(x^2 - 5x \right) + x^3 \right] \left(-\dfrac{1}{x\sqrt{x}} + \dfrac{3}{8} \sec^2 3x \right)$

$\qquad + \left(\dfrac{2}{\sqrt{x}} + \dfrac{1}{8} \tan 3x \right) \left[-(2x - 5) \sin\left(x^2 - 5x \right) + 3x^2 \right]$

4. $y = 3^{4.7x^2}$

$\dfrac{dy}{dx} = 9.4x \cdot \operatorname{Ln} 3 \cdot 3^{4.7x^2}$

5. $f(x) = \dfrac{e + x^6}{\csc x^4 - \sec x^3}$

Using the Quotient Rule and remembering that e is simply a numerical constant :

$$f'(x) = \frac{\left(\csc x^4 - \sec x^3\right)\left(0 + 6x^5\right) - \left(e + x^6\right)\left(-4x^3 \csc x^4 \cot x^4 - 3x^2 \sec x^3 \tan x^3\right)}{\left(\csc x^4 - \sec x^3\right)^2}$$

$$f'(x) = \frac{\left(\csc x^4 - \sec x^3\right)\left(6x^5\right) - \left(e + x^6\right)\left(-4x^3 \csc x^4 \cot x^4 - 3x^2 \sec x^3 \tan x^3\right)}{\left(\csc x^4 - \sec x^3\right)^2}$$

6. Since perpendicular lines have negative reciprocal slopes, the line must have a slope of -5.

7. $\displaystyle\lim_{x \to 3} \frac{x^3 - 27}{x - 3}$

$\displaystyle\lim_{x \to 3} \frac{(x-3)(x^2 + 3x + 9)}{x - 3}$

$\displaystyle\lim_{x \to 3} (x^2 + 3x + 9) = 3^2 + 3(3) + 9 = 27$

8. $f(x) = \sin x; \qquad x = 0 \text{ and } x = \pi$

$V = \displaystyle\int_0^\pi \pi \left[f(x) \right]^2 dx$

$V = \displaystyle\int_0^\pi \pi \left[\sin x \right]^2 dx$

$V = \displaystyle\int_0^\pi \pi \sin x^2 \, dx$

$V = \left[\pi \left(\dfrac{1}{2} x - \dfrac{1}{4} \sin 2x \right) \right]_0^\pi$

$V = \left[\pi \left(\dfrac{1}{2} \pi - \dfrac{1}{4} \sin 2\pi \right) \right] - \left[\pi \left(\dfrac{1}{2}(0) - \dfrac{1}{4} \sin 2(0) \right) \right]$

$V = \pi \left(\dfrac{1}{2} \pi - \dfrac{1}{4}(0) \right) - \pi \left[-\dfrac{1}{4}(0) \right]$

$V = \dfrac{1}{2} \pi^2 - 0$

$V = \dfrac{1}{2} \pi^2 \approx 4.93$

9. $y = \tan\left(\sqrt[3]{u} + u\right); \quad u = e^{2-x} + \text{Ln } x$

$y = \tan\left(u^{\frac{1}{3}} + u\right)$

$\dfrac{dy}{du} = \left(\dfrac{1}{3}u^{-\frac{2}{3}} + 1\right)\sec^2\left(u^{\frac{1}{3}} + u\right) = \left(\dfrac{1}{3\sqrt[3]{u^2}} + 1\right)\sec^2\left(\sqrt[3]{u} + u\right)$

$\dfrac{du}{dx} = -e^{2-x} + \dfrac{1}{x}$

$\dfrac{dy}{dx} = \dfrac{dy}{du} \cdot \dfrac{du}{dx}$

$\Rightarrow \dfrac{dy}{dx} = \left(\dfrac{1}{3\sqrt[3]{u^2}} + 1\right)\sec^2\left(\sqrt[3]{u} + u\right)\left(-e^{2-x} + \dfrac{1}{x}\right)$

Inserting the original expression for u:

$\dfrac{dy}{dx} = \left(\dfrac{1}{3\sqrt[3]{\left(e^{2-x} + \text{Ln } x\right)^2}} + 1\right)\sec^2\left(\sqrt[3]{e^{2-x} + \text{Ln } x} + e^{2-x} + \text{Ln } x\right)\left(-e^{2-x} + \dfrac{1}{x}\right)$

10. $\displaystyle\int_0^{\frac{\pi}{2}} \left(\sin x + \cos x\right) dx = \left[-\cos x + \sin x\right]_0^{\frac{\pi}{2}}$

$= \left(-\cos\dfrac{\pi}{2} + \sin\dfrac{\pi}{2}\right) - \left(-\cos 0 + \sin 0\right)$

$= (0 + 1) - (-1 + 0)$

$= 2$

11. $\displaystyle\int \dfrac{5}{e^{6x}} dx = \int 5e^{-6x} dx$

$= -\dfrac{5}{6}e^{-6x} + C$

$= -\dfrac{5}{6e^{6x}} + C$

12. $\displaystyle\int_{-1}^{4} \frac{x^2 - x - 6}{x - 3}\, dx = \int_{-1}^{4} \frac{(x-3)(x+2)}{x-3}\, dx$

$$= \int_{-1}^{4} (x+2)\, dx$$

$$= \left[\frac{1}{2} x^2 + 2x \right]_{-1}^{4}$$

$$= \left[\frac{1}{2}(4)^2 + 2(4) \right] - \left[\frac{1}{2}(-1)^2 + 2(-1) \right]$$

$$= (16) - \left(-\frac{3}{2} \right)$$

$$= 17\frac{1}{2}$$

13. $\displaystyle\int \sec^2 5x\, dx = \frac{1}{5} \tan 5x + C$

14. $\displaystyle\int \frac{dx}{\sqrt{x-7}}\, dx = \int (x-7)^{-\frac{1}{2}}\, dx$

$$= 2(x-7)^{\frac{1}{2}} + C$$

$$= 2\sqrt{x-7} + C$$

15. Using integral form #10 :

$$\int \frac{\sin^3 x}{8}\, dx = \frac{1}{8} \int \sin^3 x\, dx$$

$$= \frac{1}{8} \left[-\frac{1}{3}(2 + \sin^2 x)\cos x + C \right]$$

$$= -\frac{1}{24}(2 + \sin^2 x)\cos x + C$$

16. $\displaystyle\int_0^{\frac{\pi}{4}} 2x \underbrace{\cos x \, dx}_{dv}$, $\underbrace{2x}_{u}$

$u = 2x$ $\qquad\qquad dv = \cos x \, dx$

$\dfrac{du}{dx} = 2$ $\qquad\qquad \dfrac{dv}{dx} = \cos x$

$du = 2 \, dx$ $\qquad\qquad v = \sin x$

$$\int u \, dv = uv - \int v \, du$$

$\Rightarrow \displaystyle\int 2x \cos x \, dx = 2x \sin x - \int \sin x \, (2dx)$

$$= 2x \sin x - \int 2 \sin x \, dx$$

$$= 2 \sin x + 2 \cos x + C$$

$\Rightarrow \displaystyle\int_0^{\frac{\pi}{4}} 2x \cos x \, dx = \left[2x \sin x + 2 \cos x + C \right]_0^{\frac{\pi}{4}}$

$$= \left[2\left(\frac{\pi}{4}\right)\sin\frac{\pi}{4} + 2\cos\frac{\pi}{4} + C \right] - \left[2(0)\sin 0 + 2\cos 0 + C \right]$$

$$= \left[\frac{\pi}{2}\left(\frac{\sqrt{2}}{2}\right) + 2\left(\frac{\sqrt{2}}{2}\right) + C \right] - \left[0 + 2(1) + C \right]$$

$$= \frac{\sqrt{2}\,\pi}{4} + \sqrt{2} + C - 2 - C$$

$$= \frac{\sqrt{2}\,\pi}{4} + \sqrt{2} - 2 \approx 0.52$$

17. $\cos x^2 y + \sqrt{x^2 + y^2} = e^{x+y}$

$\cos x^2 y + \left(x^2 + y^2\right)^{\frac{1}{2}} = e^{x+y}$

$\left[x^2 \dfrac{dy}{dx} + y(2x)\right]\left(-\sin x^2 y\right) + \dfrac{1}{2}\left(x^2 + y^2\right)^{-\frac{1}{2}}\left(2x + 2y \dfrac{dy}{dx}\right) = \left(1 + \dfrac{dy}{dx}\right)e^{x+y}$

$-x^2 \dfrac{dy}{dx}\sin x^2 y - 2xy\sin x^2 y + \dfrac{x}{\sqrt{x^2 + y^2}} + \dfrac{y\dfrac{dy}{dx}}{\sqrt{x^2 + y^2}} = e^{x+y} + \dfrac{dy}{dx}e^{x+y}$

$-x^2 \dfrac{dy}{dx}\sin x^2 y + y\dfrac{dy}{dx} - \dfrac{dy}{dx}e^{x+y} = e^{x+y} + 2xy\sin x^2 y - \dfrac{x}{\sqrt{x^2 + y^2}}$

$\dfrac{dy}{dx}\left(-x^2\sin x^2 y + \dfrac{y}{\sqrt{x^2 + y^2}} - e^{x+y}\right) = e^{x+y} + 2xy\sin x^2 y - \dfrac{x}{\sqrt{x^2 + y^2}}$

$\dfrac{dy}{dx} = \dfrac{e^{x+y} + 2xy\sin x^2 y - \dfrac{x}{\sqrt{x^2 + y^2}}}{\left(-x^2\sin x^2 y + \dfrac{y}{\sqrt{x^2 + y^2}} - e^{x+y}\right)}$

18. $\int_1^3 \frac{1}{x}\,dx;$ $\qquad n = 8$

$$h = \frac{b-a}{n}$$

$$h = \frac{3-1}{8}$$

$$h = 8$$

$\Rightarrow$ $x_0 = 1.00$ $\qquad f(x_0) = f(1.00) = \frac{1}{1.00} = 1.0000$

$x_1 = 1.25$ $\qquad f(x_1) = f(1.25) = \frac{1}{1.25} = 0.8000$

$x_2 = 1.50$ $\qquad f(x_2) = f(1.50) = \frac{1}{1.50} \approx 0.6667$

$x_3 = 1.75$ $\qquad f(x_3) = f(1.75) = \frac{1}{1.75} \approx 0.5714$

$x_4 = 2.00$ $\qquad f(x_4) = f(2.00) = \frac{1}{2.00} = 0.5000$

$x_5 = 2.25$ $\qquad f(x_5) = f(2.25) = \frac{1}{2.25} \approx 0.4444$

$x_6 = 2.50$ $\qquad f(x_6) = f(2.50) = \frac{1}{2.50} = 0.4000$

$x_7 = 2.75$ $\qquad f(x_7) = f(2.75) = \frac{1}{2.75} \approx 0.3636$

$x_8 = 3.00$ $\qquad f(x_8) = f(3.00) = \frac{1}{3.00} \approx 0.3333$

$$\int_1^3 \frac{1}{x}\,dx \approx \frac{0.25}{3}\left[\begin{array}{l}1.0000 + 4(0.8000) + 2(0.6667) + 4(0.5714) + 2(0.5000) + 4(0.4444) \\ +2(0.4000) + 4(0.3636) + 0.3333\end{array}\right]$$

$$\int_1^3 \frac{1}{x}\,dx \approx \frac{0.25}{3}\left[\begin{array}{l}1.0000 + 3.2000 + 1.3334 + 2.2856 + 1.0000 + 1.7776 + 0.8000 \\ +1.4544 + 0.3333\end{array}\right]$$

$$\int_1^3 \frac{1}{x}\,dx \approx \frac{0.25}{3}(13.1843)$$

$$\int_1^3 \frac{1}{x}\,dx \approx 1.0987$$

19. $\displaystyle\int \frac{x^2}{\sqrt{x^2-100}}\,dx$

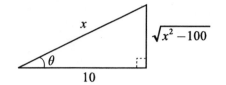

$u = a\sec\theta$

$x = 10\sec\theta \qquad\Rightarrow\qquad x^2 = 100\sec^2\theta$

$\dfrac{dx}{d\theta} = 10\sec\theta\tan\theta \qquad\qquad x^2 - 100 = 100\sec^2\theta - 100$

$dx = 10\sec\theta\tan\theta\,d\theta \qquad\qquad x^2 - 100 = 100\left(\sec^2\theta - 1\right)$

$$x^2 - 100 = 100\tan^2\theta$$

$$\sqrt{x^2-100} = \sqrt{100\tan^2\theta}$$

$$\sqrt{x^2-100} = 10\tan\theta$$

$$\int \frac{x^2}{\sqrt{x^2-100}}\,dx = \int \frac{100\sec^2\theta}{10\tan\theta}\left(10\sec\theta\tan\theta\,d\theta\right)$$

$$= \int 100\sec^3\theta\,d\theta$$

$$= 100\left(\frac{1}{2}\sec\theta\tan\theta + \frac{1}{2}\,\mathrm{Ln}\left|\sec\theta + \tan\theta\right| + C\right) \quad \text{(from the Table of Integrals on pg. #172)}$$

$$= 50\sec\theta\tan\theta + 50\,\mathrm{Ln}\left|\sec\theta + \tan\theta\right| + C$$

From the triangle,

$$\tan\theta = \frac{\sqrt{x^2-100}}{10}$$

$$\sec\theta = \frac{x}{10}$$

$$\Rightarrow \int \frac{x^2}{\sqrt{x^2-100}}\,dx = 50\left(\frac{x}{10}\right)\left(\frac{\sqrt{x^2-100}}{10}\right) + 50\,\mathrm{Ln}\left|\frac{x}{10} + \frac{\sqrt{x^2-100}}{10}\right| + C$$

$$= \frac{x\sqrt{x^2-100}}{2} + 50\,\mathrm{Ln}\left|\frac{x\sqrt{x^2-100}}{10}\right| + C$$

$$= \frac{x\sqrt{x^2-100}}{2} + 50\,\mathrm{Ln}\left|x + \sqrt{x^2-100}\right| - 50\,\mathrm{Ln}\left|10\right| + C$$

The Book of Problems - CALCULUS

20. $\int \dfrac{4x-3}{\sqrt{4x^2-6x+3}}\,dx = \int \left(4x^2-6x+3\right)^{-\frac{1}{2}}(4x-3)\,dx$

$$u = 4x^2-6x+3$$

$$\frac{du}{dx} = 8x-6$$

$$du = (8x-6)\,dx$$

$\Rightarrow \int \left(4x^2-6x+3\right)^{-\frac{1}{2}}(4x-3)\,dx = \dfrac{1}{2}\int \left(4x^2-6x+3\right)^{-\frac{1}{2}}2(4x-3)\,dx$

$$= \frac{1}{2}\int \underbrace{\left(4x^2-6x+3\right)^{-\frac{1}{2}}}_{u^{-\frac{1}{2}}}\underbrace{(8x-6)}_{du}\,dx$$

$$\frac{1}{2}\int u^{-\frac{1}{2}}\,du = \frac{1}{2}\left[2u^{\frac{1}{2}}+C\right] = u^{\frac{1}{2}}+C = \sqrt{u}+C$$

Reinserting the original expression for u:

$$\int \frac{4x-3}{\sqrt{4x^2-6x+3}}\,dx = \sqrt{4x^2-6x+3}+C$$

21. $y = x^3 zw^4 + e^{xwz}$

$$\frac{\partial y}{\partial x} = 3x^2 zw^4 + wze^{xwz}$$

$$\frac{\partial y}{\partial z} = x^3 w^4 + xwe^{xwz}$$

$$\frac{\partial y}{\partial w} = 4x^3 zw^3 + xze^{xwz}$$

22. $y = x^5 + e^{x-2} + \sin\left(x^2-7x+3\right)$

$$\frac{dy}{dx} = 5x^4 + e^{x-2} + (2x-7)\cos\left(x^2-7x+3\right)$$

$$\frac{d^2y}{dx^2} = 20x^3 + e^{x-2} + (2x-7)\left[-(2x-7)\sin\left(x^2-7x+3\right)\right] + \cos\left(x^2-7x+3\right)\cdot 2$$

$$\frac{d^2y}{dx^2} = 20x^3 + e^{x-2} - (2x-7)^2\sin\left(x^2-7x+3\right) + 2\cos\left(x^2-7x+3\right)$$

23. $\displaystyle\int_1^6 2x^2\,dx;$ $n = 10$

$h = \dfrac{b-a}{n}$

$h = \dfrac{6-1}{10}$

$h = \dfrac{5}{10}$

$h = 0.5$

$\Rightarrow$ $x_0 = 1.0$ $f(x_0) = f(1.0) = 2(1.0)^2 = 2.0$

$x_1 = 1.5$ $f(x_1) = f(1.5) = 2(1.5)^2 = 4.5$

$x_2 = 2.0$ $f(x_2) = f(2.0) = 2(2.0)^2 = 8.0$

$x_3 = 2.5$ $f(x_3) = f(2.5) = 2(2.5)^2 = 12.5$

$x_4 = 3.0$ $f(x_4) = f(3.0) = 2(3.0)^2 = 18.0$

$x_5 = 3.5$ $f(x_5) = f(3.5) = 2(3.5)^2 = 24.5$

$x_6 = 4.0$ $f(x_6) = f(4.0) = 2(4.0)^2 = 32.0$

$x_7 = 4.5$ $f(x_7) = f(4.5) = 2(4.5)^2 = 40.5$

$x_8 = 5.0$ $f(x_8) = f(5.0) = 2(5.0)^2 = 50.0$

$x_9 = 5.5$ $f(x_9) = f(5.5) = 2(5.5)^2 = 60.0$

$x_{10} = 6.0$ $f(x_{10}) = f(6.0) = 2(6.0)^2 = 72.0$

$$\int_1^6 2x^2\,dx \approx \frac{0.5}{2}\left[\begin{array}{l} 2.0 + 2(4.5) + 2(8.0) + 2(12.5) + 2(18.0) + 2(24.5) + 2(32.0) + 2(40.5) \\ + 2(50.0) + 2(60.5) + 72.0 \end{array}\right]$$

$$\int_1^6 2x^2\,dx \approx \frac{0.5}{2}\left[2.0 + 9.0 + 16.0 + 25.0 + 36.0 + 49.0 + 64.0 + 81.0 + 100.0 + 121.0 + 144.0\right]$$

$$\int_1^6 2x^2\,dx \approx \frac{0.5}{2}(647.0)$$

$$\int_1^6 2x^2\,dx \approx 161.8$$

24. $f(x) = \dfrac{3}{x}$

$$f'(x) = \lim_{\Delta x \to 0} \frac{f(x + \Delta x) - f(x)}{\Delta x}$$

$$f'(x) = \lim_{\Delta x \to 0} \frac{\dfrac{3}{x + \Delta x} - \dfrac{3}{x}}{\Delta x}$$

$$f'(x) = \lim_{\Delta x \to 0} \frac{\dfrac{3x - 3(x + \Delta x)}{x(x + \Delta x)}}{\Delta x}$$

$$f'(x) = \lim_{\Delta x \to 0} \frac{\dfrac{3x - 3x - 3\Delta x}{x(x + \Delta x)}}{\Delta x}$$

$$f'(x) = \lim_{\Delta x \to 0} \frac{\dfrac{-3\Delta x}{x(x + \Delta x)}}{\Delta x}$$

$$f'(x) = \lim_{\Delta x \to 0} \frac{-3}{x(x + \Delta x)}$$

$$f'(x) = \frac{-3}{x(x)} = -\frac{3}{x^2}$$

25. $\cos^2 x \dfrac{dy}{dx} - 2 = 0; \quad y = -11$ when $x = \dfrac{\pi}{4}$

$$\cos^2 x \frac{dy}{dx} - 2 = 0$$

$$\cos^2 x \frac{dy}{dx} = 2$$

$$\frac{dy}{dx} = \frac{2}{\cos^2 x}$$

$$\frac{dy}{dx} = 2\sec^2 x$$

$$\frac{dy}{dx} \cdot dx = 2\sec^2 x \cdot dx$$

$$dy = 2\sec^2 x \, dx$$

$$\int dy = \int 2\sec^2 x \, dx$$

$$y = 2\tan x + C$$

calculation cont. on next page...

Solution #25 from previous page...

Inserting the initial conditions we find C:

$$y = 2\tan x + C$$

$$-11 = 2\tan\frac{\pi}{4} + C$$

$$-11 = 2(1) + C$$

$$-9 = C$$

The particular solution is therefore:

$$y = 2\tan x - 9$$

26. $f(x) = \frac{1}{3}x^3 - 4x + 6$

$f'(x) = x^2 - 4$

$$x^2 - 4 = 0$$

$$(x+2)(x+2) = 0$$

$$x + 2 = 0 \qquad x - 2 = 0$$

$$x = -2 \qquad x = 2$$

Points of interest: $x = -2$ and $x = 2$

$f''(x) = 2x$

$f''(-2) = 2(-2) = -4 < 0 \qquad \Rightarrow \qquad$ a relative maximum occurs at $x = -2$.

$f''(2) = 2(2) = 4 > 0 \qquad \Rightarrow \qquad$ a relative minimum occurs at $x = 2$.

27. $f(x) = 2e^{10x}$

$f'(x) = 20e^{10x}$

$f'(0) = 20e^{10(0)} = 20e^0 = 20(1) = 20$

The slope of the tangent line at $x = 0$ is 20.

28.

a) $y^2 = x$

$\sqrt{y^2} = \sqrt{x}$

$y = \pm\sqrt{x}$

Because of the $\pm$ sign, each x is associated with two different y's. Therefore, the equation is not a function.

b)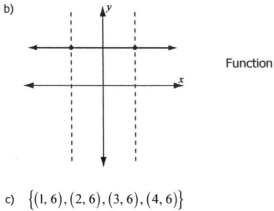

Function

c) $\{(1, 6), (2, 6), (3, 6), (4, 6)\}$

Domian $= \{1, 2, 3, 4\}$

Range $= \{6\}$

Each domain element is associated with a single range element. Therefore, the relation is also a function.

29. $y = \tan \sqrt{x^3 - 3}$

$y = \tan\left(x^3 - 3\right)^{\frac{1}{2}}$

$\dfrac{dy}{dx} = \dfrac{1}{2}\left(x^3 - 3\right)^{-\frac{1}{2}}\left(3x^2\right)\sec^2\left(x^3 - 3\right)^{\frac{1}{2}}$

$\dfrac{dy}{dx} = \dfrac{3x^2}{2\sqrt{x^3 - 3}}\sec^2\sqrt{x^3 - 3}$

$dy = \dfrac{3x^2}{2\sqrt{x^3 - 3}}\sec^2\sqrt{x^3 - 3}$

30. $\displaystyle\int_{-3}^{2}\int_{0}^{2}\int_{-1}^{1}(x+y-z)\,dz\,dx\,dy$

Evaluating the innermost integral:

$$\int_{-1}^{1}(x+y-z)\,dz = \left[xz+yz-\frac{1}{2}z^2\right]_{-1}^{1}$$

$$= \left[x(1)+y(1)-\frac{1}{2}(1)^2\right]-\left[x(-1)+y(-1)-\frac{1}{2}(-1)^2\right]$$

$$= \left(x+y-\frac{1}{2}\right)-\left(-x-y-\frac{1}{2}\right)$$

$$= 2x+2y$$

$\Rightarrow \displaystyle\int_{-3}^{2}\int_{0}^{2}\int_{-1}^{1}(x+y-z)\,dz\,dx\,dy = \int_{-3}^{2}\int_{0}^{2}(2x+2y)\,dx\,dy$

Next, we evaluate the integral with respect to dx:

$$\int_{0}^{2}(2x+2y)\,dx = \left[x^2+2xy\right]_{0}^{2}$$

$$= \left[(2)^2+2(2)y\right]-\left[(0)^2+2(0)y\right]$$

$$= 4+4y$$

$\Rightarrow \displaystyle\int_{-3}^{2}\int_{0}^{2}\int_{-1}^{1}(x+y-z)\,dz\,dx\,dy = \int_{-3}^{2}(4+4y)\,dy$

Finally,

$$\int_{-3}^{2}(4+4y)\,dy = \left[4y+2y^2\right]_{-3}^{2}$$

$$= \left[4(2)+2(2)^2\right]-\left[4(-3)+2(-3)^2\right]$$

$$= 16-6$$

$$= 10$$

Thus,

$$\int_{-3}^{2}\int_{0}^{2}\int_{-1}^{1}(x+y-z)\,dz\,dx\,dy = 10$$